They Would

Not

Be Moved

They Would

Not

Be Moved

by

Harvey Yoder

The cover art is not intended to be historically accurate, but rather the artist's interpretation of a scene from one of the stories.

Cover Painting: Marianna Heule, Michigan
Cover design: HeuleGordon, Inc. Grand Rapids, Michigan

Editorial Committee
Alvin Mast, Lois Miller, David Troyer
Proofreaders
Rachel Mast, Wilma Dueck, Tabitha (Beachy) Schmidt, Silvia Tarniceriu, Michael Jantzi, Philip Troyer

ISBN 1-885270-23-2

Printed in the USA

To order additional copies of *They Would Not be Moved*, please contact:
TGS International
PO Box 355, Berlin Ohio 44610 USA
Phone: 330-893-2428
Fax: 330-893-2305

For more information about **Christian Aid Ministries**, see pages 201-202

Preface

This is a companion book to *They Would Not Be Silent*: it also consists of a collection of short stories from Romania and the former Soviet Union. I have included explanatory notes at the beginning of each chapter to familiarize the reader with the setting of that story. It has again been a pleasure to collect the information for these stories and an inspiration to hear how God moved in the lives of His children during communism.

All of these stories are based on actual happenings and incidents. I have used my imagination where no details were given or where memories could not supply needed information. I take full responsibility for any errors that may have occurred.

Even though these stories are unique, we can identify with the very human emotions and feelings that our Christian brothers and sisters experienced. None of these people have sought glory for themselves, but have shared their stories with us in order that we, too, can grasp the reality of Christ's nearness in our lives.

Although we may never experience the trying situations these people did, we still need the same Source of life to direct us.

A special thanks to the people who helped make this book possible:

- The Executive Committee at Christian Aid Ministries that has supported this venture

- David Troyer, General Director of Christian Aid Ministries

- Tabitha (Beachy) Schmidt, for her expertise in editing the manuscript

- Alvin Mast, Lois Miller, Rachel Mast

- Silvia Tarniceriu, for introducing many of the people in this book, for her valuable work as an interpreter and guide during my stay in Romania, for her labors in checking for accuracy of content, and for her warm friendship

- Andre and Tanya Pronin, our dear Ukranian friends who acted as hosts, coordinators, and interpreters during my stay in their home

- Michael Jantzi, the "Ukrainian" editor who used his keen mind to spy out discrepancies in the stories

- My wife, Karen, and our daughter, Marianne, who endured the loneliness of separation while I roamed on another continent gathering information, and who went through the uncertainties of the attack on America on September 11, 2001 while I was overseas

- To all the people featured in this book who freely shared their testimonies with me

- Most of all, I thank You, Jesus, for loving me and giving me the strength to complete this book. May You receive all honor and glory for what You have done!

Harvey Yoder
74 Vaughn Road
Spruce Pine, NC 28777
harveyoder@juno.com

Foreword

"Then shall they deliver you up to be afflicted, and shall kill you: and ye shall be hated of all nations for my sake." Matthew 24:9

Ever since the Lord Jesus Christ died for us on the cruel cross of Calvary, His people, the Christians, have also suffered and died for their faith. In Europe, from the 1500s to the 1700s, thousands of our Anabaptist forefathers endured persecution and gave their lives for the cause of Christ. But perhaps the bloodiest period of all was the recent twentieth century.

From 1917 to the 1980s, in the Soviet Union and its puppet states of Eastern Europe, untold millions of people perished under the evils of atheistic communism. Among these multitudes were many thousands of our brothers and sisters in Christ. Of the things they suffered, how they were able to remain true to Christ, and under what circumstances they died, we know but little.

These people were not spiritual giants. They were ordinary people like you and me. Under extreme stress, torture, and threat of death, not all remained faithful. But those who did left a rich spiritual legacy and notable examples for us to learn from. By being willing to die, they showed us how to live. They were cold, hungry, lonely, and threatened with death. Some spent decades in prisons or slave labor camps. But when it came to their faith, *they would not be moved.*

During the same period that many Christians in the East lost their earthly possessions, were torn from their loved ones, and gave their lives for their faith, we, their brothers and sisters in the West, experienced unparalleled material prosperity. God is sovereign. Neither they nor we chose where to be born. But, in the final analysis, who suffered the most?

All across Eastern Europe and the vast former Soviet Union, thousands of stories are waiting to be told. Each year fewer and fewer people remain alive to tell them. This is to our loss.

Here at Christian Aid Ministries we feel compelled to capture at least some of these stories. Why? To help us in the West gain a better understanding of what it has cost others to be Christians. To inspire us to new heights in our own spiritual experience. And, to encourage us that it is possible to remain faithful, and even prosper spiritually, in the midst of persecution.

Will persecution ever come to America? Only God in His wisdom knows.

Maybe these stories will help us ask: "What am I really living for? Am I a stranger and pilgrim on this earth, looking for a city whose builder and maker is God? Do I have a faith that would be worth dying for? Do I know Jesus, not only as my *Savior*, but also as *Lord* of my life? Do others *know* I love Jesus?"

This is the second in a series of books about what our brothers and sisters experienced as they tried to remain true to their Lord. It is our prayer that God may be honored and His name glorified as you read the accounts of Christians who had the testimony of *they would not be moved.*

David N. Troyer
General Director,
Christian Aid Ministries

Table of Contents

1

The Red Rose

Around thirty years ago, a sheltered girl was thrust into an environment that horrified her pure heart. Then God sent a special message in the form of a flower.

*N*atasha* moved her left leg slightly to relieve the pressure from a small twig under her knee. She listened intently to Brother Vins' prayer as he led the believers in a closing meditation. They were holding communion in secret, so his words, strong and true, were spoken in a semi-hush.

In all of her twenty-three years, Natasha knew only of meeting in secret for worship with the believers. In the winter, they met in houses and apartments, but hardly ever the same home in succession. In the summer, they met in the forest, where welcoming trees surrounded them protectively. Natasha loved these times. A sense of danger accompanied them every time they met, for it was illegal to meet without approval from the authorities. Many times their meetings had been interrupted by the police, but usually a warning had been passed along in time for the entire group to melt into the shadowy forest in all directions.

* Refer to glossary on pages 204-206 for pronunciations or definitions of italicized words.*

This was a special Sunday. Months had gone by since they had held their last communion service. Several times, communion had been scheduled, but every time something came up to prevent the church from gathering. But, today had been different.

From the beginning, the very heavens had smiled upon the group of almost 200 people. The June sun was pleasantly warm. A breeze stirred the treetops, moving the leaves in a constant rustle of sound, muffling the singing of their hymns.

Natasha's naturally cheerful disposition responded to the beauty of the day, and with joy welling up in her heart, she had been spiritually refreshed. For more than five hours they had been together, singing, praying, and commemorating the death and resurrection of Jesus Christ. Brother Vins' sermon was encouraging and uplifting.

Perhaps it was the beauty of the day and the privilege of being "caught up into heavenly places" that made the group of worshipers oblivious to the outside world. Certainly, the kneeling believers were not prepared for the loud shouts and harsh cries from a group of men bursting out of the woods and rushing toward them.

"We caught them in the act!" one officer yelled as he rushed over to Brother Vins. "Here is the leader! We caught him!" As *Georgi* Vins knelt before the Lord, the man stepped on his outstretched legs with his heavy boots.

The intruders gathered around him and the other men facing the congregation. Frightened cries from the children and the women mixed with the shouts and curses of the twenty men that surrounded the brothers.

Natasha felt a stab of fear. She rose swiftly to her feet as the confusion increased. Another man had joined the officer in holding down Vins. "We know you are the leader of this illegal group. This time we have you!"

A man dressed in civilian clothes was taking pictures of the crowd. "We have caught you in your drunken party," he yelled exultantly as he focused his camera on the table holding the communion bread and wine. "Now we have proof of what you do when you get together for your parties!"

Natasha could see that Brother Vins was now on his feet. In the melee, a group of the believers moved close to their pastor. Before the officers realized what was happening, they quietly pushed between Vins and his captors. Some of the mothers were slipping away among the trees with their children. In a few minutes, a tight group of more than a hundred men and women, with Vins in the middle, were standing in the clearing, surrounded by the officer and his men.

"Forward! You are under arrest for plotting against the government!" The officer brandished his arms vigorously as he led them through the woods.

"Take courage, sister! The Lord is with us!" Natasha heard the quiet words of comfort from a middle-aged brother she knew only slightly. His calm acceptance of the circumstances quieted Natasha's racing heart.

But when they reached the train tracks, and she saw a group of ten more officers waiting for them, she clutched her throat in fear. And when they were herded like so many cattle into a closed train car, tears stung her eyelids.

"Natasha!" She turned just in time to see her friend Tanya come toward her in the crowded car before the heavy metal door slammed shut. She groped in the dark and found her friend. Wordlessly, they hugged each other tightly.

When the guards opened the door of the car after a brief journey on the train, they were met with a wave of song from the captives.

" . . . trials and temptations,
        Is there trouble anywhere?
We will never be discouraged,
        Take it to the Lord in prayer!"

"Quiet!" The commanding officer roared. His face became red as he shouted to be heard above the singing.

They were escorted from the car and into the huge train station of Kiev, then out into the street again. The people in the station looked at them curiously as they filed through the station.

Natasha heard an officer yelling at the crowds gathered to watch this strange procession of over a hundred people being escorted away from the train station and down the street. People crowded the sidewalks to gawk.

The group had just emerged from an underpass when a tour bus lumbered toward them. Through the open windows, tourists were peering out. When the bus was right beside the captured believers, one of them began to sing and the others joined in. As the bus slowly drove on, the tourists inside were surrounded by singing.

"Do thy friends despise, forsake thee?
  Take it to the Lord in prayer.
In His arms He'll take and shield thee,
  Thou wilt find a solace there."

This time the officer did not dare shout at them to be quiet. These tourists were foreigners who had been told that the citizens of Ukraine enjoyed complete religious freedom. Indeed, the curious spectacle of over a hundred citizens being marched along the city street, and singing a hymn, was going to raise enough questions. But as soon as the bus was out of sight, he screamed at them to be quiet. Then, a new disturbance began.

Without warning, a group of ten officers suddenly forced themselves into the middle of the group and headed for Georgi Vins. As soon as the brethren saw what was happening, they surrounded their pastor. The crush of bodies was pushed up against a chain link fence, and the struggling officers pushed and shoved at the wall of brothers.

Natasha was suddenly filled with boldness. She wedged herself along the edge of the human barricade and faced the officers. Her back was against the fence and she linked herself tightly with the others surrounding Vins.

The heaving, pushing officers began swearing and shouting at them. "Stand aside! Get away! You are obstructing justice!"

Vins was in the middle of the group of believers that faced the officers. Not a single person moved.

The officers stared at them belligerently, then with another rush, they tried to force themselves through the group to get at Vins.

Natasha found herself face to face with a short, stocky officer with a crew cut. His sweaty face was only inches away. He tried to wedge himself past her to get to Vins. Natasha refused to move. With an angry yell, he raised his arm and swung at her head. Natasha ducked.

The man yelled in pain as his hand hit the metal fence. With a vicious glare, he pushed her hard, jamming her cruelly against the fence.

Now the officers began to beat at the believers with their clubs. They swarmed into the crowd and shoved aside anyone in their way. Natasha was grabbed by the arm and pushed along the sidewalk. Her captor, the man with the crew cut, was extremely angry. He forced her into a near run.

At the police station, they kept only twenty of the men. But Natasha was not released with the rest of the women. Her personal escort saw to that. His eyes, full of hatred, glared venomously at her. Every once in a while, he would look malevolently at the bruise on his hand where he had hit the fence.

Then, suddenly, he took her into a small office. Now he had her where no one could see or hear what happened.

As soon as he had shut the door, his suppressed rage erupted. He slammed the unsuspecting girl against the wall. Natasha cried out as her head hit the wall. Before she could recover from the impact, she felt a stinging blow on her back.

"Please, don't!" Her cry of anguish filled the room. "Oh, please!"

The officer gave no attention to her pleas. Again and again, he beat her about the shoulders and on her back. Tears of pain began streaming down her cheeks. "Oh, Lord, please help me! Save me!"

"Comrade *Stanislav*! Stop this at once!" Natasha heard a new voice behind her.

The beating continued. Blow after blow hit between her shoulder blades. Natasha writhed in pain.

"Stanislav! If you kill this girl, you will be in deep trouble!" The new voice spoke with authority.

Dimly, through her pain, Natasha heard her tormentor reply, "She attacked me and bit my hand!"

"Stop at once, I tell you! You are not the one to decide what punishment to give her. Write out a report against her and let the chief of the police deal with her."

Through the long night, Natasha waited. Her head ached and her back was sore from the beating. She sat in the hall with the brethren, but no one dared to speak. There were only twenty-one of them now.

One by one, the brethren were led into the chief of police's office. Sometimes yells and shouts were heard through the closed door. More than once, Natasha heard the thud of clubs striking against a body. She shivered and wept softly. She prayed wordlessly.

After a moment of silence inside the room, the door opened, and another brother was taken in. Then the door closed again.

Twenty times the door opened, a brother was taken in, and then the door closed. Natasha was last. Sore, tired, and frightened, she hardly knew what was happening. The wonderful time they had in the forest seemed like a long time ago. She wondered if her mother was safe at home with the younger children. She asked God to give her mother strength; she prayed for herself. She felt all alone.

Then the door opened for the last time. She was the only one waiting in the hall.

"Girl, it's your turn." The officer looked at her, not unkindly.

She was scarcely in the room before she heard laughter. She looked in alarm at the chief of the police.

He was sitting behind his desk, looking up at her. "Sit down," he gasped between gales of laughter.

Natasha sat numbly on a wooden chair, facing the desk. She stared in disbelief at the laughing man.

"What a joke! When I read the report that Comrade Stanislav wrote about his assailant, I pictured this Amazonian-type woman who threatened the life of Stanislav and viciously bit him." Again he roared with laughter. "Now, here comes this petite blue-eyed damsel! You must be some tigress!"

He mopped his forehead and, chuckling, read the report again. "You must have really bit him hard to make him write this huge report about you." He looked at her with respect.

"Sir," Natasha found herself saying. "Sir, I did not bite him. He tried to hit me and when I ducked, he hit his hand against the chain link fence."

The chief looked at her sharply. He read the report again. "You did not attack him? You did not bite his hand viciously with those little white teeth of yours?"

Natasha looked straight into his eyes. "No, sir, I did not."

A moment of silence followed.

"Miss, I feel sorry for you. Somehow you got mixed up in this. You are such a pretty young girl. But because you have been arrested with the others, you will be sentenced to prison. Perhaps I can influence the Secretary of Religious Affairs to give you only a light sentence. Surely you cannot be dangerous enough to be locked away for three years."

Natasha felt the calm presence of the Spirit. "I will accept whatever the Lord sees best for me."

"Aren't you afraid of prison?"

"Sir, I have lived with the thought of prison ever since I was young. When I was five, my father was put in prison because he preached the truth from the Bible. I remember thinking even then that God is close to those who suffer for Him in prison. I determined that when I was older, I, too, would be happy to suffer for my Lord, even if it meant prison."

"You do not know what you are saying! Have you ever even seen the inside of a prison?"

Natasha shook her head. But she looked calmly into his eyes.

"Such a shock you will have. I can see by the pure expression in your pretty blue eyes that you have not been exposed to the horrors that are in our prison. I would do anything to keep you from finding out. But that is not in my department." He wrote briskly, yelled for the guard, and stood up from his desk.

"Pray to your God that you will not need to suffer. It would be such a waste of a pure, young life."

The first thing that hit Natasha as they entered the prison hall was the heat. Waves of torrid air pressed down on her until she could scarcely breathe. It had been hot in the cell where she had been kept before her court trial, but nothing compared to this. Never in all her life had she experienced such a horrible, sticky heat. She forced herself to breathe slowly as she followed the woman guard down the hall.

But it got worse. By the time they reached the cell door and the guard opened the barred gate with her key, Natasha thought she would faint. She panted for breath.

At times in her young life she had tried to imagine what hell must look like, especially after a minister had preached vividly about the terrors awaiting the unsaved. But never had she even come close to imagining a scene as appalling as the one before her now.

In the murky light, she saw women inmates scattered around the large room. Bunk beds lined all the walls, except for a small space where there were several holes in the cracked concrete floor. This was the toilet, exposed for all to see. The smell of raw sewage mingled with the oppressive heat. Natasha swallowed with difficulty, trying not to gag.

Some of the prisoners were sitting on the floor in the middle of the room, playing a wild card game. Their loud, rough yells and screams flowed into every corner of the cell. They scarcely looked up from their game as Natasha was shoved inside and the door locked behind her.

Water! Natasha looked around wildly for a spigot. She had to have water!

She saw a woman turn away from a corner opposite the toilets, wiping her mouth on her bare arm.

Natasha walked over to the water pail. A tin cup, chained to the bars, hung down above the water bucket. Her hand reached for the cup, then faltered. The tin cup was scarred with teeth marks. She looked into the water bucket. A faint odor reached her nose.

With a shudder, Natasha turned away. She could not make herself drink from that water. She would rather suffer thirst. At least for now.

As her eyes became adjusted to the darkness, she saw the rest of the prisoners in her cell. Lying on the bunks, slumped on the floor, leaning against the metal framework of the beds, the women were in all stages of undress. Many of them, trying to escape the heat, had thrown all their clothes off.

Natasha tried to look away after her first horrified glance, but there was no safe place to look. She searched each bunk for a space where she could sit down. But no bunk was empty. Natasha felt her head reel.

Out of the score of faces listlessly looking at her, a young girl's face swam into focus. Above the grime and neglect of her prison uniform, dark hair framed a pretty face. Something in her eyes welcomed Natasha.

Then, the girl moved slightly to one side of the bunk. That was enough of an invitation. Natasha stepped around several women on the floor and hesitantly walked toward the slight sign of welcome.

"Thank you," she breathed softly as she settled down on the little space. For a moment, the air was not so heavy, so stifling. She drew a ragged breath.

That was a mistake. The odor of the decaying straw mattress beneath her rose up in an overpowering wave.

Natasha shook her head and closed her eyes. If only the smells weren't so horrible! How could she stand fifteen days in this awful place? What ever had made her think she could endure prison for several years? Why, she wasn't sure she could even stay alive for two weeks here! How long would it be before she could make herself drink that awful water? And she could not imagine that she would be able to choke down any of the prison "slop," as the food was called. Already, in the cell where she had been before her trial, the food had been mostly inedible. Surely, in this terrible place, it would even be worse.

Natasha felt despair wash over her. Tears welled up behind her tightly closed eyes.

"Why are you here?" The words were soft, even kind.

Natasha looked up.

Her bunkmate was looking at her curiously. The girl sat cross-legged, hunched over so her head would not hit the mattress above them.

"I was arrested along with some others because we were having communion in the forest," Natasha said simply. "The officers broke in among us and took us by train to Kiev. Most of the young people were released, but one officer insisted I had bit his hand, so he filed a report against me."

"Did you? Bite his hand, I mean?"

Natasha shook her head. "No, I didn't. He wanted to push past me and when I didn't move, he tried to strike me. I ducked, and he hit his hand against a metal fence. Hard!"

The other girl barked a short laugh. "Served him right!"

After a moment, the girl asked, "Why were you having a service in the forest?"

Natasha looked into the dark eyes across from her. "You see, we are not registered with the State, as a church, so when we meet, our services are considered illegal. But we meet anyway."

"Why?"

Natasha found herself groping for words. "Because it is right for us. We have the right to meet as we feel led of God. The government does not have the authority to tell us if we may meet or not. We need to meet for worship." She did not know if she made sense or not.

In the silence that followed, Natasha was suddenly aware of prisoners in the neighboring bunks who had become quiet and were listening to her.

"Well, I would just stop meeting if it meant trouble with the law," the girl beside her said. "It would not be worth time in prison for me."

Natasha felt a boldness creep over her. "Well, I want to serve my Lord, Jesus Christ. Even though I was raised in a believing home, there came a time when I realized that I, personally, must make a decision to follow Jesus. I repented of my sins and asked the blood of Jesus to cleanse me."

One of the older women snorted. "You don't look like you even know what sin is, young girl. A face as pure as yours surely doesn't even know sin."

"I thought that way at one time," Natasha answered. "Then one time during a sermon in the forest, the Spirit showed me I was wrong. I not only needed to repent from the sins I had committed, I needed the blood of Jesus to make me righteous before God. I sensed the great love that Christ has for me—such a great love that it made Him willing to give His life for me on the cross!"

A group of more than ten women were listening. Natasha spoke simply, gaining strength as she talked. "You see, no one is ever good enough on their own. All of us have sinned, and need a Savior, regardless of how good we have been."

"I don't understand," another woman said. "My mother never sinned. She was the godliest woman that ever lived."

"Huh, she sure messed up when she had you, then. You don't even know who your father is!"

An argument broke out as a clamor of voices rose up, defending their own views.

"Look!" A woman with a scarred face and a fierce stare came striding up. She poked her face down under the bunk to where Natasha was sitting. "You pretty little thing, wise up!" She shoved a clenched fist against Natasha's nose. "You stir up trouble in here, you get to eat fist!" She pushed against Natasha's face menacingly with her clenched hand.

Natasha cringed. She tried to shrink against the wall.

"Shut up! I mean it! Shut up and keep your ideas to yourself!" Then with a glare, she included all the other women. "That goes for all of you! We will not have a riot and bring the guards in here with their clubs!"

With a final jab of her fist in Natasha's direction, she left.

Natasha did not dare stir from her bunk all evening. She kept licking her lips whenever a desire for water became almost overpowering. She tried not to see the women around her, lolling about in indecency. Snatches of conversations reached her as the voices rose and fell in listless, complaining monotony.

Her ears were assaulted with curses and swearing. Filthy words poured out of the degenerate prisoners' mouths. Modesty and decency seemed unknown to them as they talked of things that caused Natasha's cheeks to burn in shame and humiliation. She covered her ears in horror.

The girl on the bunk beside her watched her with a cynical smile. Finally, she spoke.

"You really are a sheltered girl, pet. I can see what you hear is cutting into your heart like a knife. Have you never had a boyfriend?"

Natasha looked once more at the girl. "No," she whispered. "I am waiting for God to lead me to the right person. Or, He may never want me to get married."

This time, the dark-haired girl's face became grim. "I don't know where God comes into the picture. But I wish I had been brought up like you. I wouldn't be in the trouble I am now if I would never have had boyfriends."

She talked in a low tone to Natasha. "Every day on my way to the college where I studied, I passed this policeman. He began speaking nicely to me, and I guess I kind of flirted with him, just a little. I thought it was fun to have an officer pay attention to me.

"Well, for him, things were more serious, so one day he asked me to go out with him in the evening. I got scared and told him I couldn't. I tried going another way to my school, but he knew where I attended, and started waiting for me when school was out.

"One day, we had an argument after I told him I was not interested in him. I stuck my tongue out at him and he got mad.

"The next day, I was arrested on charges of spying for an organization in the West. I was tried, and sentenced to fifteen days here in prison. I saw that policeman in the courtroom and I know it was he who had trumped up the charges against me. When I get out of here, I will make sure he never sees me again."

They heard the sound of the meal trolley outside their cell. A rush of women surged toward the bars. Natasha's companion left the bunk and joined the throng.

In the frenzy of noise, Natasha heard the sound of a male voice. She looked up and saw that a man had brought the evening food.

Then in shame and disgust, she pressed her hands over her ears. Never, in her wildest imaginations, had she thought any female would use such horrible and filthy language. She felt a revulsion rise from deep within her soul. She ground her teeth to try to drown out the lewd, ribald words that filled the entire room.

In spite of her efforts, she heard the guard's voice rise in a raucous laugh. His deep voice, as he joked and taunted the women, penetrated Natasha's efforts to stifle the words that seared into her brain.

She was shaken to the core. Stretching out on the mattress against the wall, she lay rigid with fear and shame. Even after everyone else was bedded down for the night, and the dark-haired girl lay tight beside her in the sticky confines of the cell, she could not sleep.

Snatches of overheard conversations came back to her, over and over. She tried to block out the words, shut her mind to the images that came to her, and stifle any suggestions as to what the overheard words meant, but to no avail.

She couldn't pray. She had no words. She could only groan in agony as again and again, her mind repeated the words she had heard.

"Hold still," her bunkmate muttered. "You will push me right out of bed."

Natasha forced herself into rigidity. She could not antagonize the only one in the whole room who had shown kindness to her. She lay still, frozen in fear and horror.

She forced her mind to go back to the trial. Only three days before.

The woman judge had given the sentences. First, the brethren had been sentenced. "Georgi Vins, 15 days. *Vasily Pruitin*, 15 days." On down the list, the brethren had been sentenced for a mere fifteen days. Then, at the end, she had heard her name: "Natasha *Stuchyov*, 15 days."

It had come as a surprise to most of them, especially the pastor and the elders of the church, that their sentence was so light. But someone had smuggled information to them that word of their arrest and trial had spread to the West, and the Soviet government was faced with the embarrassing predicament of what to do with the people they had arrested. They hoped that by giving the believers a minimum sentence of fifteen days, they would appear lenient to the western world, but still convey a threat to the twenty-one who were arrested.

"Thank the court for their lenience," the judge had instructed Natasha.

"Comrade Judge, I do not thank the court," Natasha had spoken up bravely. "Your sentence of fifteen days indicates that I am a criminal and will appear on my records as such." She had been well educated by her father's many prison terms and harassments. "A longer sentence would indicate that I am disloyal to this country and am considered a threat to it. But, I would also be stating my loyalty for the spiritual kingdom of Heaven. I would count this as an honor to my Lord and King!"

The judge had looked at Natasha with respect. This young girl with blue, blue eyes and soft, curly, brown hair was no ignorant person. There was a ring of confidence and sincerity that impressed her.

"You do not know what you say, young girl. Obviously you have not yet been exposed to the condition of our prisons. You will learn soon enough. Fifteen days will be long enough to expose you to a side of life you never imagined." Then, hardening her voice, she continued. "I hope prison will change your mind about your religious fanaticism and make you think twice about attending illegal meetings."

Natasha had been dismissed and brought to this place. This sweltering, reeking, evil place.

Natasha tried to keep the tears from squeezing out as she lay on the foul-smelling bunk. She dared not give in to a storm of weeping. Even though her head was beside the feet of her bunkmate, she knew she would wake the other girl if she would be overcome with weeping.

All night long, she battled with her thoughts until she thought she would go crazy. Like demons, filthy words she had overheard assaulted her weary mind. Crazy images danced through her consciousness until she felt her tense nerves scream.

Over and over, she prayed the simple phrase, "Lord, save me! Lord, save me!"

But still, the women's voices and the leering laughter of the guard penetrated her mind. To her tortured mind, the voices and laughter were more like the voices of Satan and his cohorts.

Sobbing quietly to herself, her mind clung to an incident the night after her arrest. She had wanted to pray, but was too afraid to kneel on the floor in her isolation cell. She had heard of the mice and rats and other pests inhabiting the cells. So instead, she had huddled, cowering, on the bunk. Then she heard a kind voice come through the door of her cell.

The glaring lightbulb had illuminated her every movement, and the guard had seen her terror. "Young girl, do not be afraid. You will soon be released."

She never knew whether he had just been trying to be kind to her, or had really known that she would receive a short sentence. But his words had been a comfort to her then.

Now there was no kind voice. Just these terrible words and scenes hammering against her mind. As she remembered her own words in the courtroom, asking for a longer sentence, she wept silent tears. How could she ever have thought she would be brave enough to endure the ravages of prison for a year or two? Now she wasn't sure she could keep her sanity for the remainder of the fifteen days.

Natasha felt utterly spent. No solace, no comfort, came her way. Every time she tried to remember Bible passages or hymns, a wash of evil and vile words swept through her mind again. She felt powerless against the onslaught of filth that engulfed her.

All she could think of the next morning when another day started was, "How can I stand this? Oh, Lord, how can I take more of this?"

A thin gruel, along with an insipid tea, had been passed out for breakfast. Natasha could not make herself swallow any of the gruel, but sipped her lukewarm tea without enjoyment. The heat that had diminished only slightly during the night began to build up again.

"Young girl! Hey, you with the blue eyes! Come here!"

At first, Natasha did not realize that anyone was calling to her. Then some of the women began shouting at her.

Outside the bars, in the corridor, stood a young man beckoning to her. Dressed in uniform, he looked vaguely familiar to Natasha.

She hesitantly went over to him. He was holding out a red rose toward her. "Your brothers in prison sent this to you. They are thinking of you and praying for you."

As if in a dream, Natasha took the proffered rose. She buried her nose into its center and inhaled long and deeply. The sweetest fragrance she had ever smelled filled her nose and swept through her entire being.

Slowly, she lifted her eyes to the guard. Now she remembered. He was the same one who had comforted her the night after her arrest. She looked down at the rose again.

Dimly, vaguely, she heard the taunts and suggestive words flung at her from the other women. But they came as though from a great distance, and the filthy words and implications no longer tore across her mind like destructive missiles from hell. A wonderful feeling of peace and protection enveloped her.

She took the rose back to her bunk. Miraculously, she was left alone. Where the dark-haired girl was, she did not know.

How carefully she held her precious gift. Trying to make sure she did not exhaust the fragrance, she drew in short breaths, as though taking small sips of some delicious nectar. Her lips gently kissed the velvety petals. She stroked the soft sides against her cheek. The five green leaves on the stem were a perfect foil for the rich red of the flower. She did not even mind the thorns on the stem. So exquisite was her rapture over the rose that she hardly felt the small pricks of pain.

Again and again, she buried her nose deep into the middle of the rose, closing her eyes against the sordid conditions around her. She was transported into a world all her own—just her and a red, red, rose.

Snatches of song came to her. Bible passages brought a healing balm to her soul. "Fear thou not, for I am with thee . . . I will strengthen thee; yea, I will help thee . . ."

Natasha could pray again. "Oh, Lord, thank You so much for sending me this lovely red rose! You are ministering to me in my despair by giving me something beautiful to remind me. Oh, how much You love me! Thank You, Jesus!"

The rose became a symbol of God's love for her. In the night, when she woke in terror as she remembered where she was, reaching out and touching the rose she had carefully hung upside down from the mattress above her brought reassurance. During the day, even after the fragrance of the rose began to fade and the flower itself began to droop, Natasha still clung to the wonder of God's love to her in her greatest need.

Then, before her two weeks were over, she found that she no longer needed the rose. She knew that God had sent her the velvety flower to remind her of how much He loved her. As she responded to His message, she found her strength coming from the Source of love and no longer from His gift. She marveled at the goodness of the Lord in nurturing her weak faith at a time when she needed something to cling to. Now, her faith in her Savior, her Lord, was strengthened, and she could live above the sordid conditions of her cell.

The water was still terrible, the food still nearly inedible, and the cell conditions still almost unbearable, but Natasha could now face it by herself. No, not by herself, for the Spirit of the Lord was with her. She did not need to face anything by herself anymore! She was never alone. Jesus said, "I will never leave thee, nor forsake thee."

The red rose also portrayed another truth to the pure, sheltered girl from a believer's home.

All her life she had been exposed mostly to men and women of pure characters, noble in their desire to serve God. In the worship services, she had been surrounded by people of God, who poured out their hearts and lives for the cause of the Gospel.

Then, in prison, through the filthy, depraved speech of the women prisoners, she was exposed to the dark side of sinful mankind. These spoken scenes had sickened and disgusted her to the degree that she had felt humiliated and shamed in front of any man. Her purity of mind had been lost.

Through the gift of the red rose, Natasha's reason was restored. No longer did she feel unclean and violated when she came into the presence of men. "Your brothers have sent you this rose." When the young guard had said this, God had allowed her to once again see her spiritual brethren, strong and noble in their manhood, standing for the truth. These heroes were willing to endure the horrors of prison for their faith. They, too, had to endure the filth and unbridled passions of fellow prisoners. But they, like Daniel in the Bible, refused to give in to anything that would grieve their Lord.

So, this was the message God allowed Natasha to see in the simple gift of the red rose. That message stayed with the young girl for the rest of her brief stay in prison. At her release, it was a wiser woman who emerged from her trial, than the young girl who had entered the dark doors fifteen days earlier.

But the red rose went with her. Dried now, and devoid of fragrance, it remained a token for years to come of how her Lord showed His love to her in her darkest hour.

Later, she thanked Brother Vins for sending her the gift. He was puzzled and told her he had never sent her a rose while she was in prison. How could he, when he was in prison himself? No, none of the other brethren knew anything about it, either. Not even *Anatoly*, the young man she would later marry, had the slightest idea of who had sent the rose.

So, how did the rose find its way to the hot, smelly, dank concrete cell of the women's prison and into Natasha's despairing life? No one knows for sure.

For Natasha, one thing is sure. God saw that she needed some affirmation of His love for her, some reminder of the pure hearts of His saints. So He sent the guard to search her out and give her what she needed—in the form of a beautiful red rose.

2

Cargo in Jeopardy!

This is just one segment of a journey of Bibles. Marcel told me the story himself and even though it happened more than fifteen years ago, he still gives glory to God for His deliverance in spite of his own negligence in getting enough sleep!

The headlights of his car stabbed into the dark, illuminating the road ahead of him. Marcel was so tired. He had left Siret in northern Romania at three o'clock the afternoon before, driven all the way down to *Ploiesti*, loaded up the car, and was now headed back home. It was after midnight, the time it was hardest for him to stay awake and be alert.

Marcel glanced over at his traveling companion, *Valentin*. Bless him. He had come along to be a companion on this trip. But now Valentin was sleeping.

Pulling himself up sharply on the driver's seat, Marcel tried to shake the sleepiness from his brain. His body cried out for rest. His eyelids were heavy, drooping down across his vision. Maybe if he would just close one eyelid at a time, he could find some relief. He had to get back to Siret so he could report for work in the morning. No one must suspect that he had even taken this trip. His cargo was too precious, too expensive to have anyone question what he was doing so far away from home. So far away from *Viorica*, his wife, and the children . . .

With a jerk, *Marcel* was instantly awakened by a loud, roaring noise! Blinding headlights, shining directly into his sleep-fuddled face, were coming straight for him!

Instinctively, Marcel jerked the steering wheel to the right. Praise God. They were going to miss the lumbering truck! With a thankful heart, Marcel guided his speeding car past the noisy truck and on into the darkness.

The next thing he knew, he heard Valentin groan. He felt numb, and something was pressing into his side. The car was no longer running, and all was silent except for his companion's moans of pain. Headlights shone crazily against a concrete bridge abutment. They were his headlights.

They had had an accident. They had hit the side of a bridge. Marcel's mind slowly registered the facts.

Dimly, Marcel remembered the truck. He remembered missing the noisy monster, and then, nothing. He could not remember anything after that.

What about the cargo they carried in the trunk and in the back seat? Every empty space had been filled up.

Marcel felt packages pushing against the back of his head. He felt something beside him on the seat. Dimly, he could see shapes pushed up against the shattered windshield.

Again, Valentin groaned.

"Valentin!" Anxiety for his friend's welfare brought Marcel out of his stupor. "Valentin! Are you all right? Are you hurt?"

"Oh-h-h!" Valentin groaned. "My head! My head! Get me out of here!"

Frantically, Marcel shoved at the packages all around him. He pushed the parcels into the space behind him to get to his friend.

But he was trapped. He could not free himself to help Valentin. Gritting his teeth against his own pain, he struggled once again.

Headlights came toward them. A car slowed down and the driver's head poked out the window in alarm.

Marcel panicked. He wrestled against the heavy packages and desperately shoved at them. No! No one must see what they had! They must free themselves from this wreck and get away from here! It was too dangerous! They would be put in jail! They would never see their families again!

"God, help! Oh, help!" Marcel's cry of desperation went winging upwards through the dark night.

"Careful now! Take it easy!" The driver of the passing car was beside Marcel. He had seen Marcel's struggle to free himself. "I'll jerk the door open, and then help you out. Calm down, now!"

Marcel fell back exhausted. It was over. There was no chance of escape.

With a wrench, the rescuer opened the door beside Marcel. The warm night air rushed into the wrecked car and washed over Marcel's aching head.

It took only a moment for the man to free Marcel from behind the pushed-in steering wheel. Then he left Marcel and tried to go around the other side of the car to free Valentin.

But he was back almost instantly. Urgency was in his voice as he said, "I'll have to get him out on this side. Your car is balanced on top of the concrete wall and I can't get to him from there!"

Marcel stood groggily on his feet. He swayed back and forth. He could not seem to steady himself enough to help.

Then, Valentin was out. He, too, seemed dazed and Marcel could see blood oozing out of a cut on his forehead. Their rescuer led him to the side of the road, and made him sit down.

Their cargo! Marcel tried to open the back door of the car. He pulled on the latch, but it did not open. He was too weak.

A flicker of lights came from behind them. Another vehicle! Marcel almost sobbed as he pressed himself close to his wrecked car. No! They must not stop! They must not!

An ambulance! How did it happen that an ambulance came through here at this time of the night? Then, to his horror, another vehicle stopped, and a loud voice was asking what had happened.

"Where are the victims? Are there any survivors?"

No! It was a policeman! Marcel felt all his energy ebbing away, leaving him completely drained. It was all over! Already, the prison cell seemed to be closing in around him, cutting him off from his wife and family. The cargo! The packages! They would somehow trace them back to the people who had brought them this far! Marcel groaned in anguish, not for his injuries, but for the predicament they were in. He was putting a whole network of people in danger.

"Yes, there are two survivors," their rescuer shouted out. "Both hurt! Over here!"

An ambulance worker bent over Valentin. She checked his pulse, then briefly examined the cut on his head. "Put him in the ambulance," she ordered her assistant.

"There's another one over there!" the driver told them, pointing toward Marcel.

"Ah, I'm not hurt that badly," Marcel stammered as the lady came toward him. "I think . . . I'll be . . . be fine." Marcel tried to speak calmly in spite of his rapidly beating heart. His head had cleared and he was trying to appear as normal as possible. He could not leave the car. Not here, all by itself, with no one to watch over the cargo. No, he could not leave!

"Are you sure?" the ambulance worker questioned. Marcel could hear the doubt in her voice. "The way that car looks, I don't see how you can even be alive, much less unhurt."

"I'm fine. Maybe some scratches, but that's nothing. Take my friend to the hospital and get him taken care of. He must be hurt worse than I am."

The ambulance left. The policeman shone his powerful flashlight on the wrecked *Dacia*. Marcel winced when he saw how clearly the light shone through the back windows.

"There is not much left of your car," the policeman said in wonder as he beamed the light on the front. The hood of the car was bent back at a crazy angle. The whole right side of the car was pushed back in a jumble of broken parts. Water from the radiator dripped out and formed a puddle on the dark road.

Marcel joined him. Maybe the policeman would leave and he could somehow get rid of the cargo. Maybe he could hide it somewhere.

Marcel reached out to steady himself with his left hand. He exhaled sharply as he felt pain shooting up his arm. He grabbed his wrist and squeezed tightly.

"What's wrong? You are hurt!" The policeman shone his flashlight onto Marcel's wrist. "Let me see!"

Marcel reluctantly exposed his left wrist. A flap of skin was folded back, exposing the tendons on the underside of his lower arm.

The policeman looked hastily away. "I can't stand the sight of blood," he said faintly. "I'm taking you to the hospital."

"I can't leave the car," Marcel protested. "Everything will be gone—be stolen by the time I get back!"

The policeman looked around in the early morning light. "Get in my car," he commanded. "I'll get the man from that store over there to watch over your car. Do you have something valuable in there?"

"I—I have a tape recorder in there," Marcel stammered.

"Well, right now you need to go to the hospital. Let the store owner guard your stuff."

Marcel was numb on his ride to the hospital. Wordlessly, he prayed all the way.

———————————

"You need to stay several days," the doctor told Marcel after he had finished stitching the flap of skin in place. "You must have had a slight concussion, and several of your ribs are cracked."

Marcel listened through a haze of pain. So that was why he could not think clearly. He must have hit his head against something, erasing his memory of the accident.

He tried to sit up.

"You must rest." Firm hands pushed him back onto the cot. "You are still drowsy from your concussion and you could get worse if you don't hold still. Now stay right there and I will get a nurse to wheel you to a room." The doctor went over to the sink to wash his hands. "I will come in and check up on you on my morning rounds. You will need to stay quiet," he emphasized again.

But as soon as the doctor went out the door, Marcel sat up. He swung his feet over the side of the bed and waited several moments until his head stopped swimming. Then, he cautiously stood up and walked to the doorway. He held onto the wall beside the door.

Slowly, he peered into the hallway. No one was in sight. Marcel made a right turn and went toward the entrance. He tried not to hurry, but at any moment he expected to be called back by the hospital staff.

Thankfully, there was no one at the front desk, and he was able to slip out unnoticed. The night air felt good after the strong, antiseptic smell of the hospital.

The city was just waking up. Hardly anybody was out on the street, and Marcel was confused. He did not remember which roads the policeman had used to bring him to the hospital and he had never been in this part of the city before. In fact, he did not know much about the city of Ploiesti at all. When he came in to pick up his cargo, he had turned his car over to another man, then lay down in the back seat so he would not know where they were going. He did not take his place in the driver's seat of the packed car on their return trip until they came to the edge of the city. It was safer that way. If he should be stopped and questioned about where he had gotten his packages, he could always tell them truthfully that he did not know.

But now he had a problem. How was he to get back to his wrecked car? And once he was there, what was he going to do with all the packages? A barrage of questions hammered against his mind, pushing his physical ailments into the background.

A street sweeper came toward him, briskly plying her twig broom in front of her.

"Excuse me, please," Marcel stopped her. "Can you tell me the best way to get to the north side of the city, to go toward—uhm—toward *Suceava*?"

The lady stopped and leaned on her broom. "Well, sir, I have lived in Ploiesti all my life, but I tell you, I have never been outside this city. You see, we were all raised together, my brothers and sisters and I with my widowed mother, and we never had the privilege to get around like some folks do." She grinned at him. "But we always had enough to eat. Even if it was *mamaliga* every morning and every evening. I got to like—"

Marcel tried again. "Excuse me. I just need to know which way to go to get to the north side of the city. Can you tell me?"

This time the lady closed her eyes in thought. "I think right that way." She pointed behind her. "If that is north," she concluded doubtfully. Then she brightened. "Here comes *Lenuta*! She will know."

Lenuta did know. She directed Marcel in the opposite direction that the street sweeper had, and he gratefully thanked her.

Would anyone stop to pick him up? Marcel looked down over

his clothes and realized he must look quite a sight. His shirt was streaked with blood. His pants were torn and his arm was in a splint. He sighed and held out his hand, giving the classic sign of the hitchhiker.

To his relief, a concrete truck screeched to a stop. Marcel opened the door and asked the driver if he was going to the north side of the city. At his brief nod, Marcel climbed in and sat down. The driver shifted gears and they started through the streets that were now bright with early morning sunshine.

"Had an accident?"

"Yes," Marcel answered ruefully. "I fell asleep and hit a bridge." He had to yell to be heard above the noise of the truck motor.

"Car totaled?"

"Afraid so."

By the time they reached the wrecked car, Marcel was pleasantly surprised to see that Valentin was already there. Even more surprising was the fact that the car was completely empty of packages. Not a parcel was in sight!

"Where did you put them?" was Marcel's first question.

"Under the bridge," Valentin replied tersely. "Had to get them out of there."

"Praise God," Marcel replied. "I worried so much about what would happen with both of us gone. I prayed constantly, but I must confess, I was still afraid. Actually, I still am."

Valentin nodded. "Me too," he confessed. "There still are a lot of unanswered questions. Like, how do we get all those packages up north without being discovered?"

The two men bowed their heads. "Lord," Marcel prayed, "You see the predicament we are in. We need Your direction and guidance on how to get out of this situation and deliver our cargo safely to its destination. We will trust You to get us out of this mess. We ask this in Jesus' name." Weary, plagued with pain and feeling helpless, the two men stood in silence as they waited. Their responsibility weighed heavily on them.

The police car pulling up at the scene was not a welcome sight. With a heavy heart, Marcel turned toward the officer.

It was the same one who had been there hours earlier. "I need to fill out a report of the accident," he told them kindly. "Come with me to the station." He motioned for both of them to get into his car.

The police station was only a short distance up the road. They followed the policeman into his office and sat down.

"Let me see your documents."

Marcel had been dreading this. He did not have documents! They had been taken away only the day before when a policeman had stopped him for passing a horse and wagon. There had been a solid yellow line on the road, but Marcel had felt free to quickly dart around the slow-moving hay wagon. However, the policeman who stopped him had obviously not considered it safe, and confiscated his documents. Marcel, knowing that his contacts in Ploiesti were waiting for him, had decided to risk traveling without his papers.

The policeman looked up from his paper. "Your documents," he repeated. "Oh, they are in the car."

Marcel felt hot. "Sir, I can give you the information by memory."

"Sure, sure," the officer replied genially. He obviously felt sorry for the battered men.

Valentin nudged Marcel with his knee. He turned his head slightly toward the window.

Marcel's heart sank as he followed Valentin's gaze. He swallowed and felt anxiety sweep over him again.

Village children were darting in and out from under the bridge! Even at this distance, the two men could see them excitedly running toward the small village with their parcels!

"Sir, is it all right if my companion goes back to the car? I see some children around there, and they might—they might be taking things!" Marcel could not refrain from making the request.

The officer looked out the window. "Sure," he replied easily. "I will take you back after I am finished here."

Valentin left, almost on the run. But Marcel could see that he was too late. The children had already disappeared with their loot.

The report filed, Marcel stood. "I can walk back," he suggested hopefully.

"No, no!" the policeman objected, "I will take you back."

After they got back to the wrecked car, Marcel said, "Thank you, sir. You have been most kind." Marcel got out of the officer's car, hoping that he would leave them alone now.

"Your car is totaled, I'm afraid. What will you do with it?" the policeman asked sympathetically. "You are a long way from home, aren't you?"

Marcel nodded. He did not say anything. He, too, wondered what to do. But one thing he did know; he wanted the officer to leave.

Valentin had disappeared under the bridge. He probably did not realize they were back, the policeman included.

"There's your extra gas can." The policeman got out of his car. "It must have landed down there after you hit the side of the bridge." He pointed down the bank where the flat metal can lay in the tall grass. "You won't need that gas now. Could you pour it into my tank?" Even for policemen, it was not always easy to buy gas in communist Romania.

Marcel was already headed down the grassy slope. He wanted Valentin to hear him. "Sure, sure," he said loudly. "You might as well take the rest of the gas. We won't be needing it for this car!"

"Your papers and books are lying there too!" the policeman called out. "Get them. You may need them!"

Marcel felt his face get hot again. Quickly he snatched some small pamphlets and stuffed them inside his shirt front. He gathered two black books that had been sprawled upside down in the grass and tucked them under his splint. Then, hastily, he grabbed the gas can and climbed back up to where the policeman was waiting.

"Here," he panted, extending the metal can. "You can pour it in better than I can with only one hand."

The shouts of children made him swivel his head toward the bridge. The boys and girls were coming back again carrying the packages with them!

"Thank you for the gas," the officer said, handing the empty can back to Marcel. "I must leave now. I hope you can find a way home."

With a sigh of relief, Marcel watched the disappearing car.

"We brought the books back to you," came the voices of the excited children. "Our mothers said we may not keep them. They are holy books!"

They crowded around Valentin, who was still under the bridge. "Where did you get them? They are not in our language!"

"Would you help us put them back in the car?" Valentin asked. "We need to get them all back in."

Willingly, they helped. In a flash, they scurried up the bank with the parcels, which Marcel packed back into the wrecked car. Some of the paper wrappings had split and black books were lying in loose piles. The children cheerfully helped gather them all together and gave them to Marcel.

"That's all," they shouted as Valentin followed them up the bank. "The holy books are now back in the car!"

They went squealing away in delight after Marcel handed them a few coins.

"Now what?" Marcel looked at his friend.

"While you were gone," Valentin said tersely, "I remembered that there is an old sister living here in this village. We will tow the car to her yard. Then we will have to re-pack the books and take as many as we can by train."

The old woman asked no questions after Valentin briefly explained what had happened. He did not tell her what their errand was, and she did not ask. Years of experience had taught them it was best not to inquire about things that could incriminate someone.

They left the wrecked car behind, tied up as many books in bundles as they could carry (two bundles for Valentin, one for Marcel) and made their way to the train station.

Anxious even now, Marcel could not relax as they made their way north to Siret. Tired as he was, every disturbance, every stop along the way, brought him to alertness.

When they reached Siret that evening and delivered their packages to the accustomed place, they briefly explained to the brother what had happened.

Finally, they were ready to go home. Walking together, the two men trudged toward their waiting families. They reached Marcel's street first.

Valentin reached out and shook Marcel's good hand. "The Lord watched over us more than we ever believed possible. He must have sent a whole army of angels to protect us and our luggage."

Marcel was silent for a moment. He pressed Valentin's hand warmly. "Even the children turned into helpers. And wasn't it remarkable how the policeman acted!"

He turned up the last street, his weary steps quickening as he neared his home, his waiting wife, and small children.

That was one day in the lives of a vast number of Bible couriers. They were men and women who smuggled the Word of God. They were willing to risk going the dangerous distance from Western Europe, through country after country, to their final destination of Russia.

From the village of Siret in Romania, someone would try to take the Bibles across the heavily guarded Romanian/Russian border and into the hands of the Russian people. Marcel had no idea how all this was done. He was only one link in the vast chain of people involved in this work. In God's work.

Marcel did not give up. The day off from work was not a problem. He explained truthfully that he had been in a car accident, and no questions were asked. He repaired his car. Some months later he took more Bibles from the south to the north. He continued working hard at his job by day and making runs by night. But one thing was different. He always made sure he got his sleep. He had learned his lesson.

3

Fearful of Baptism

This story holds special meaning for me because I first heard it while our family served with Master's International Ministries in Ukraine. Mikhail, or Misha, was employed by the mission as a driver and he showed us the actual spot where he was baptized as a boy. Choosing to live for Christ was no light matter for a young man in the 1970s.

"Repent, believe, and be baptized," Brother *Anatoly* spoke sincerely to us. I could feel a longing welling up from deep within my heart. My spirit reached out to embrace the truth of our minister's words.

"Perhaps you have already repented from your sins. You have acknowledged that Jesus Christ is the Son of God. The next important step is to seal your faith with water baptism.

"For centuries, the step of baptism has meant a complete surrender to Christ. It means cutting off all ties to Satan and his kingdom. It means refusing to obey the desires and lusts of the flesh. Baptism is an outward symbol of a spiritual new birth in Jesus."

I knew this was true. I had been raised in a home where God was loved, where the Bible was believed, and where all of us children were taught in the ways of righteousness. From a child, I had been exposed to the truth.

We were meeting in the home of one of the brethren. As many

of us who could were gathered in the small living room. The house was small, and there were more than thirty people present. Even though it was summertime, the windows were all closed. It was very warm inside. I longed for the cool, night air outside.

"There is strength in obedience. All God's children sense that. That is why, when God wants us to do something, we are not completely at rest until we obey. Actually, we need to be thankful that the Lord has made us this way. It is a sign of our Father's loving care for His children. We cannot rest until we submit to the will of God."

I knew this also was true. I had not been a believer very long, only a few months in fact, and I had already experienced this. I waged a long battle before I was willing to go to my parents and confess some things I had done in my growing-up years.

I was still in my boyhood. Barely sixteen, it seemed to take me longer to mature than some other boys my age. I was rather timid and shy, not a leader, but a follower. I often regretted that I was sensitive and somewhat easily offended and hurt.

But maybe it was this that made me reach out to Christ. I knew I needed help. I wanted peace in my heart.

So, I had repented. I confessed my sins to the Lord, and invited Jesus into my heart. When I did that, I experienced a great relief. My heart had found a resting place!

"We here in our country know the cost of baptism. Many of us know of people who have been persecuted severely for their faith. Just as in New Testament times, our people know what it is to stand for their faith. As it is written, 'All that will live godly in Christ Jesus shall suffer persecution.' Many times that persecution begins when someone takes the important step of baptism. Baptism, to us, means being willing to suffer.

"We have one here with us who desires this baptism to seal his faith in the Lord Jesus Christ. *Mikhail Kobetz*, our dear young brother, has asked for baptism. We have spoken with him and we are well satisfied that Mikhail has experienced the new birth in Jesus."

A warm glow spread over my heart. The congregation smiled at me encouragingly. Yes, I was ready to make a public testimony of my belief in God and conversion. I wanted to fulfill the commandment to be baptized.

We knelt to pray. I closed my eyes tightly and prayed for courage to take a stand for Christ. I truly wanted to do the will of the Lord.

Some noise outside caught my attention. Instantly, I became extremely alert! My heart began to pound wildly as I realized what was happening. The authorities were coming! I knew it! Only they would come through the yard gate at night with such boldness.

I was at the doorway leading to the front entry, so immediately I felt trapped. The door opened behind me and three men marched right in.

I knew all three. The head of the collective farm, *Pioter Vasilyevich Khometz*, and two of the teachers from my school, Ivan *Ivanovich Golovaschenko* and *Trofim Afanasyevich Kuzmenko*. Three men whom I feared greatly.

Ivan Ivanovich took charge. "Stop this nonsense immediately! Get up off your knees! We have apprehended you right in the middle of one of your illegal meetings. You will all stay in this house until we take your names. You know that these illegal meetings will not be tolerated."

In the confusion that followed, I pressed hard against the wall. With tablet in hand, Ivan Ivanovich began writing down names. He looked at the people nearest the doorway, and he saw me.

"Kobetz! You are here too! Why should a young man be in this crowd? All the rest are old people. You young people know better. We educate you in school so you no longer need this religion, this crutch for your lives. Where is your father?"

"Sir, I am right here." My father made his way to where I was standing. I felt a little better.

"Kobetz," Ivan Ivanovich said sternly, "why do you bring your children to church? Don't you know that it is against the law for anyone under the age of eighteen to go to church? Don't you know that this is a crime, punishable by imprisonment? Why do you bring your children to church?"

"Sir, why not? It is here that they learn about God. Here they learn how to be good citizens. We teach them against the evils of drink and other sinful vices."

I knew why my father was saying this. Our village, like most other villages in Ukraine, had an extreme problem with alcoholism. More than 80 percent of the men in our villages were drunkards.

"Huh!" Ivan Ivanovich said. "I wish your children would be drunkards! They would be easier to deal with then!"

He ignored my father then and continued to write down names.

This was not difficult to do, for, even in a village of several thousand people, the head officials knew almost everyone. They kept careful records of where everyone lived and worked. They monitored as much of our lives as possible.

That is why we never had our meetings in a regular pattern. Sometimes we met on Monday night, sometimes on Friday night. Sometimes the service was at our house, sometimes at another brother's house, but hardly ever at Brother Anatoly's house. He was in enough danger for being the pastor. Our church tried hard to protect him and his family in order to keep him out of prison.

But now the officials had somehow been tipped off where we were meeting. In spite of the lateness of the day—it was now after ten o'clock—the three most important men in the village had come to break up our meeting. Break up our meeting and take down all the names of our people.

This was what terrified me. I had already suffered enough at school because I was from a believer's family, but now, it would be even worse. Ivan Ivanovich had found me at a believer's meeting.

I was right. After that evening, I was singled out for all kinds of harassments in our village school. I began to dread the very thought of school.

Things were bad at home. My father had been fined three months' wages for having been in a secret meeting, which brought extreme economic hardships to our family. The wages the collective farm paid their workers in the 1980's were mere pittances, but still, it was money. And even though we raised everything we possibly could on our little farm, we still needed to buy some things, like sugar and salt. We suffered greatly when father's wages were taken away.

But as I said, school was terrible. If I passed Ivan Ivanovich as we filed outside after classes, he was sure to make some rude remark about my believing in God. Always he would say it in such a manner as to make it clear that only the mentally deficient would believe such "fairy tales."

Once he even called me out of the line of students. "Come here, Kobetz!"

I know I looked like a beaten dog as I stood in front of him. I stared at the ground, fearing what would happen to me.

"I want all the rest of you students to look at this specimen of humanity. If we can even call him human. See how ashamed he is! No red tie to signify his allegiance to our country and the government. Because of him we have a blot on our school, a disease that continues to show how weak and foolish some of our students are. Today, we will make an example of such a disgraceful creature!"

My heart pounded in fear. I could not imagine what torture he would put me through.

"All of you! Roll up your school newspaper. As you pass this believer in God, this simpleton Kobetz, strike him! We will put the shame directly on this scumbag!"

Of course the rolled-up newspapers stung, but they did not really harm me. It was the shame, the inner hurt as my classmates filed past and hit me with the papers, that was extremely hard to endure. Some laughed at me, mocking. Others merely hit me and passed by quickly.

Every Wednesday in our weekly religion class, the lady instructor would clearly state her reason for having this class.

"We need to know about all the religions of the world. We will see how religion weakens and retards people in their education. It matters not what religion it is, Buddhism, Confucianism, Muslim, or Christian, they all make the minds of people sick and weak, believing in tales and superstitions. And since here in our school we have some who call themselves believers, we will educate you about the dangers of such false ways. The believers teach their children to close their eyes and pray to a God they cannot even see. They teach them to kneel down to worship a God they do not know. Of course, this weakens their mind and makes them simple, ignorant people."

I knew she was directing these statements against me. All the other students knew it, too. I could feel the burning red spread over my cheeks as I heard the mocking laughter and snickers of my peers. Never could I get used to these harassments, no matter how often they were repeated.

I was in a terrible dilemma. Father had told me that the ministers of the church were planning a baptism for me on Saturday. Tomorrow.

I was in mental anguish. Earlier I had been so sure, so willing to go through with baptism and to identify with the Lord's people. But now I was beginning to have doubts.

I knew what brought those doubts: the trouble that I was facing in school. Every time I was singled out for mockery and taunting by my teachers, I cringed and something inside me shriveled. I was miserable and felt intimidated all the time. Everything would get worse if the officials found out that I was baptized.

And find out they would, somehow. I was sure of that. Even though our baptisms took place in secret, often at night, somehow the news leaked out. It usually wasn't long until the entire village knew who else had joined the small band of believers in our village.

I knew it would be a terrible blow to the officials to have a young person in the village who was baptized. Sometimes the government would tolerate older people being part of the church, because they could easily explain that uneducated, ignorant people would fall for such stuff. But for a young person educated in the Soviet schools to voluntarily be baptized would be an affront to their system! Persecution was sure to rage in greater heat against me.

This is what lay at the heart of my doubts. Would I be strong enough to endure the persecutions? I knew that in my heart I was terribly fearful of suffering and pain. As bad as the mocking was at school, how could I endure further and deeper pain? I just wasn't sure I could go through with it.

So now, the night before my scheduled baptism, I told my father about my struggles. "*Misha*," he said, using the endearing nickname my family knew me by, "I have felt that you were going through these struggles, and I am praying for you. You have to know in your heart what you want to do. If you are not sure, it is better to wait. But son, let nothing persuade you that living for God is not worth all the heartaches and persecutions that come to us. God is faithful to supply all the strength we need. It may seem impossible to you now to endure persecution, but God gives us the strength when we need it, not before. What He asks of us now is to have faith that He will supply the strength whenever we need it."

I knew my decision to wait was a disappointment to my parents. But they did not make me feel guilty. Rather, they showed me love in a real and tender way. They prayed for me. They prayed with me.

Not only my parents, but the entire church, spent much time in prayer for my confusion and hesitancy. I did not feel rejection from them, only a great love. When we gathered again, late at night, to worship and pray together, many prayed for me. I was deeply touched.

But one thing I knew. I had to face this thing alone. No one else could make the decision for me.

In desperation one night, I came to God in prayer. Everything seemed to be going wrong. At school, I continued to be singled out and mocked for believing in God. All my teachers made it as difficult for me as possible. Their taunts and jeers sank deeply into my soul. I wanted to hide. After school, I wanted to avoid my family. But even when I was alone, I was not at rest. My mind continued to torment me with what was going to happen the next day at school. There was no escape.

I was all by myself in the hayloft. I pushed my face deep into the fragrant, cured hay. I wanted release for the weight lying on my heart—the weight that was making my life miserable.

"God, what shall I do? You know how scared I am of persecution. You know the misery I go through at school. How can I endure more? How can I consent to baptism if it will make all of this worse?

"Can I not just believe in You the way I am? Do I have to be baptized in water? You know my faith, my belief in You. Is it not enough that I carry on the faith of my parents and follow them? Why do I have to voluntarily do something that will only bring more and greater persecution?"

All was silent in the barn. A bullfrog croaked down by the river flowing along the edge of our little farm. The river that I would have been baptized in last Saturday if I had gone through with it.

It was as though God was silent, too. I did not sense anything from heaven, even as I waited. I wanted to hear a voice, something telling me what to do. Telling me that I did not need to be baptized, only to believe with my heart and mind.

But there was no answer. No feeling of peace about my decision to avoid baptism. All was silent.

As I lay there in the night, I talked to myself. Not out loud, just in my mind. *Actually, it would be better if I would just go along with the rest of the class in school. One thing that would make a big difference is if I would wear the red tie of the Komsomol. I could still believe in my heart whatever I wanted. But if I wore the tie, the teachers would stop making fun of me. If I would put it on just before my classes begin and take it off as soon as school is over, the trouble would end. And after I graduate from school, I won't need to wear it anymore.* I began planning in great detail how this deception could take place.

I don't know what brought me to my senses. It was as though the treachery of my own thoughts opened up a chasm so deep, so wide, that I was terrified.

"No!" I cried out. "This is a temptation from Satan! I will not do such a thing! I will not deny Jesus and pledge allegiance to a Godless government!

"Lord, forgive me! I will trust in You! I will follow You regardless of the cost. Yes, even if it means more persecution. Even if it means prison or torture! Nothing matters as much as having peace in my heart, and I know I can only have that by faith in Your strength. Faith in what You will do for me!"

Strength flowed through me. I knew what I would do. I would ask for baptism! I would ask for it soon!

Neither my parents nor anyone in church seemed surprised at my desire to move ahead with baptism. They could have cautioned me to take more time, to make sure that I would not regret it. They could have doubted my sincerity. But they did neither.

Instead, they gave their wholehearted support. Plans were made for an immediate baptism.

So, a week after my first scheduled baptism, we gathered behind our barn. In twos and threes, the brethren and sisters stole to the riverside. It was a moonless night, but no one used flashlights or lanterns. We did not want to be noticed by the neighbors.

But, I did not think too much about all that. I just knew that in my heart, I had a burning desire to be united with my brethren and sisters. I yearned to testify of my faith in Jesus. A boldness that was not from me gave me the willingness to seal my faith with water baptism, regardless of what the consequences might be.

Quietly, Brother Anatoly read from the Bible. He read the familiar passage from Acts when the Ethiopian eunuch was baptized.

As I said the words, "I believe that Jesus is the Christ, the Son of God come in the flesh, and that He died for my sins," I said them with all my heart. I knew that believing meant much, much more than just saying it now, it meant trusting in Christ for all the strength I would ever need for anything I would ever face. On my own, I could not do it. But I believed that God was able to do it for me.

Wading out into the waist-deep river, I knelt down. "Upon your confession of faith, Brother Mikhail, I baptize you in the name of the Father, of the Son Jesus Christ, and of the Holy Ghost." Brother Anatoly lowered me completely under the water.

I stood up, water streaming from my hair and clothing. Brother Anatoly embraced me and whispered, "God bless you and keep you strong, Son."

Even though it was night time, and we did not want anyone to apprehend us, the congregation began to sing softly as I waded toward the river bank.

"A talkative brook will tell my holy secret to no man;
It flows on, a cold stream through silent woods and fields.
It will not tell that the ripples heard the secret of my questing heart,
When my body was immersed in baptism at the quiet of the night;

How in the clear water for a moment my body was covered
    with water:
I was receiving a holy baptism and making a covenant with God.
I gave up evil and sin and made a promise to God by my baptism;
I promised to live for the glory of Christ. My soul rejoiced in Him.
And hearing my holy prayer that was rising from the waters to
    heaven,
And refreshing my soul with peace, God gave grace to my heart.
That stream was a speechless witness of my great secret
While light clear ripples ran over my head."

With each word, sung softly, an emotion filled me that I cannot describe. Yes! I had given myself to the baptism of water, testifying of all that Christ had done for me! Happiness flooded my heart!

My father was waiting to greet me. The other brothers came and encouraged me. My mother and the sisters from the church all crowded around me.

That night, I felt so wonderful. For some reason, I no longer feared persecution. Something had happened that gave me courage to face whatever the future would hold. I was willing to face it. Not alone, but with Jesus Christ. I had a boldness that I did not know I could possess! Praise God, my fears were gone!

Yes, after that, life was harder in some ways. Word did get out that I had been baptized, and the mocking and taunting in school got even worse. My old self still wanted to cringe and hide from the persecution, but I praise God that, many times, I could feel the courage and strength from the Spirit keeping me from despair. My parents and the church greatly encouraged me and prayed much for me. I was not always as victorious as I should have been, but even now I marvel at how God changed my fearful heart into a trusting one. He truly performed a miracle in my life.

Even though our family was continually harassed and discriminated against, I was spared from having to go through intense persecution. It was all by the grace of God and His wonderful mercy.

4

Papa's Way

The extreme poverty of the believers is something that has surfaced again and again in my interviews. Here, a loving and merciful God helped a son to take his Papa's way, through his own personal meeting with the Lord Jesus Christ.

"Stop it!" *Alexei* pushed the annoying goat away. "You may not eat my shirt!"

The white goat stuck her muzzle through the wooden slats of the stall where she was penned. Her long, pink tongue stretched beseechingly toward the young boy.

Alexei looked at the hayrack. Empty. He sighed. He knew what that meant. He would have to take the goat out and watch her while she ate the grass and weeds alongside the road.

The yard gate opened. Alexei looked out of the shed door to see who was coming. It was his father.

Mama was at the door of the whitewashed cottage before Papa reached the house. "What did they say?"

Alexei listened keenly. He saw the patience in his father's eyes as he looked at his wife. He shook his head slightly.

"Just as we feared. The judge said we must be willing to suffer for the sake of our country. He claimed the soldiers in the army are much worse off than we are."

Alexei burst out through the door. "But we can never pay 300 eggs!" His indignant voice startled his parents. "We only have five chickens! Most of the time we only get two eggs a day!"

51

"Alexei, calm down." Mama reached for her twelve-year-old son. "We know it is impossible for us to pay the 300 eggs." She put her hand on his arm.

"For us it is impossible," Papa agreed. "But for God, nothing is impossible!"

"Then I'd like to see some of those miracles!" Alexei burst out indignantly. "I'm tired of being poor because we say we trust in God. All we have is five chickens and one skinny old goat that barely gives any milk! Now we are being taxed far too much. Where are we going to get 300 eggs to fill our quota?"

Alexei's brown eyes darted back and forth between his parents' faces.

He saw his mother's eyes mist with unshed tears. She looked helplessly at her husband.

"Alexei," Papa's kind voice rebuked his son. "God has never forsaken us. In spite of the hardships we have endured, we have always, somehow, had something to eat."

"Something to eat!" Alexei repeated scornfully. "Something, but hardly ever enough!" He brushed angry tears from his eyes.

The hungry goat bleated from her stall, her complaining voice filling the little courtyard.

Without another word, Alexei turned and entered the gloomy shed. He yanked a rope from the wall and tied it to the goat's collar. Then he unlatched the door and followed the willing animal outside.

His parents had gone into the house. Alexei did not look up as he passed the open window of the lean-to kitchen. He could hear his mother moving around in the small room, preparing their next meal.

The dusty village street was enclosed on both sides with the typical wooden fences that line all Ukrainian villages. Alexei glanced listlessly up and down the street. He felt the sun shine warmly on his back. It would be hot again today.

The goat reached eagerly for some dusty grass that poked through the board fence.

"Come along," Alexei growled, jerking on the rope. "We have to get out of the village where there is something for you to eat. Everything good here is already eaten up by some other animal.

Nothing left for us."

The goat trotted willingly beside Alexei. Her ribs rippled beneath her short, white hair.

"Listen to this, Papa!" Alexei smoothed the newspaper on his knees. "It says, 'Ukraine will soon take the lead among all the countries of the world, both in agricultural and in scientific fields. Other nations are looking with longing at our rich, fertile topsoil and our fields of golden wheat. They see with what intelligence and great technological skill our trained and educated scientists have advanced beyond many of our competitors.' "

The chilly autumn wind rattled the windows. The lamp flickered as Alexei held the newspaper up slightly in order to see better.

" 'Our people will soon be living lifestyles far above anything in comparison to the capitalist countries where a few rich despots control the poor masses of workers. We will work together with our Motherland Russia and our great and wise leader, Joseph Stalin! We will succeed under his great and benevolent rule!' "

Alexei looked eagerly at his father. "I am eager to help our nation succeed, Papa! We will soon be out of our poverty and we will have enough food to eat and good warm clothes!" Alexei rubbed his hands over his worn coat.

"Alexei," Papa addressed his son, "you can't believe everything you read in the newspaper. The people who write the newspaper articles are told what to write. They must write according to the rules of the party members. We have no free newspapers in the Ukraine." He spoke gently, without any rancor.

"But surely they wouldn't write lies!" Alexei protested. "Plus, we do have rich topsoil! You know how well our garden produced last summer, how many sacks of potatoes are in the underground storage."

"Yes, son, God has blessed us with rich soil. If it were not for His providence, we would not have enough to stay alive. For this we thank God, not our nation or our rulers. They do nothing to help us."

"That's because we are believers!" Alexei said vehemently. "The other families all have plenty to eat. The men get all they want at

53

the *kolhoz*. But you can never keep a job. As soon as they find out that you believe in God, you lose your job!"

Papa bowed his head. Then he slowly answered. "Son, I know this is hard for you to understand. You are suffering the hardships because of our faith in God. Yet, you must remember that we are not always going to live on this earth. God has promised us that if we live for Him, He will take care of us in this life, and even though we suffer for Him—yes, even unto death—we have the assurance of eternal life with Him in heaven."

Alexei wrinkled his nose and turned back to the newspaper. "I choose to live a better life here on earth. Today the teacher told us to be ready to register for our *Komsomol* pledges. She will give us all the red ties to wear. We are to wear them every day for school."

There was silence in the room. Alexei could hear his mother washing the few pots in the kitchen. His older brother *Slavic* was not back from his errand. Where was he, anyway? Alexei wondered.

His father's voice came softly. "Alexei, you know how your mother and I feel about this. We want you to put your trust in God, not in man. Only God can give you what you really want. It may seem that man's way is best, but, in the end, only those who trust in the Lord for their salvation will be allowed to enter heaven."

"That's your faith. Not mine." Alexei's answer was brief. He knew his answer cut deeply into his father's heart, but he tried not to care. He had his own life to live. He was tired of living in his parents' poverty simply because they believed in God.

Besides, his teacher said there was no God. She said that only uneducated people who wanted to live in ignorance needed to believe in something they could not see.

"I will pray for you, son."

"Pray then. I will still do it."

The next morning, Alexei was sick. Too sick to go to school.

His father did not say anything to him about his words the night before. Before he put on his winter coat to leave in search of work, he paused beside the cot where Alexei lay. "I hope you will soon be better. Perhaps I can bring some better food for you today."

Alexei turned his face to the wall. Bewildering thoughts were coursing through his brain. Was he sick because of what he had said last evening? Had his father's prayers caused him to become too sick to go to school to sign up for the Komsomol?

"Alexei," his mother's voice was concerned. "I made some *kasha* for you. It is nice and hot. Do you want some milk with it? The goat is still giving us a little milk. I don't know why, because she is only eating the hay we have. It must be the Lord, for yesterday I thought she was drying up."

In spite of his aching head, Alexei was hungry. He sat up and took the bowl his mother handed to him.

"That's a lot of kasha," he said, looking at the full bowl.

"Eat all you can. It will give you strength."

"Did Papa eat any before he left?"

"Eat, son. You are growing, and you need food to give you strength."

Alexei knew the answer to his own question. Mama had divided the kasha between Slavic and him. He was sure of it. Papa had left without eating breakfast first.

It wasn't fair. No grown man should have to do without food. How could Papa work in the cold without food to give him strength?

His thoughts drifted to Slavic. Slavic had quit school and was working in the repair shop at the kolhoz. The director of the farm had recognized his mechanical ability and readily given him a job.

Slavic was hardly ever at home anymore. He stayed at the shop even after his work was over. Alexei knew his parents were grieved that Slavic was gone so much.

"Why me?" Alexei growled to himself. "Why do my parents' prayers work just for me and not for Slavic? Everything works against me."

The following day, Alexei went back to school. His mysterious illness was gone.

"This is how we are to wear it," Alexei's friend, *Tima*, told him. He took the red tie and carefully tied it around his neck.

Alexei imitated his friend. All the students were clustered around the box of ties, excitedly knotting the red cloth around their necks.

"I'm so proud of you all today," the teacher beamed at her class.

"Now you look like real people! Komsomol!"

Her glance went from student to student. Her eyes rested on Alexei.

The smile left her face. She drew her eyebrows together. "Alexei! You were not here yesterday! You did not sign your allegiance! You have no right to wear the Komsomol tie!"

Alexei was speechless. How dare she!

"I was sick!" his voice blurted out.

"Quiet!" The teacher stormed at him. "Take that tie off!" she hissed. "Only those who signed the pledge have the right to wear the tie!"

Alexei was disgusted. He knew why the teacher singled him out. It was because his parents were believers. Always, she looked for ways to mock him. She called him "the little saint" and continually heckled him about the fact that his parents went to church. "Where they pray to nothing!" she scornfully stated, time and again.

Furiously, he tried to unknot the tie. It was knotted too tightly. In a rage, he jerked it over his head and ripped the fabric.

"Alexei!" the teacher's voice was venomous. "Come with me to the director's office immediately!"

Alexei swaggered from the classroom. He would show everybody that he did not care what would happen. He winked at Tima as he left.

However, he found his knees shaking as he waited outside the director's office. He could hear his teacher's voice angrily explaining what had happened.

Then the door flew open and she sailed out. "Go in!" she commanded, and then went back to her classroom.

"Alexei! You desecrated State property! These ties cost the State money and you must not tear them. Why do you insist on not wearing a tie?" The director looked piercingly at the young student.

"I was sick yesterday, so I could not sign up with the others to become a Komsomol," Alexei replied sullenly. "The teacher said I had no right to wear one this morning since I had not signed the pledge. She told me to take it off, but it was knotted too tightly, so I tore it off." His words came out in a rush.

The director looked at his flushed face. "Would you have joined the Komsomol if you had been here yesterday?"

"Yes!" came Alexei's quick answer.

There was no immediate response. Then the director spoke. "Because you were sick and could not sign, I will inform your teacher that she must allow you to wear the tie. We need all our students to be Komsomol."

He stopped and watched for Alexei's reaction. When Alexei did not reply, but continued his steady gaze at the director, the man spoke again. "You must be punished for destroying State property. All this week you will stay after school and empty all the trash cans."

A red flush crept up into Alexei's face. He reacted against the injustice of his punishment. "I will never wear that stupid tie!" he said angrily. "It belongs to—to goats!" He could think of nothing worse to compare it with. He felt angry with the whole world.

Alexei looked triumphantly at Slavic as their parents went out the door. The two brothers lay on the cot side by side.

"They didn't even argue," Alexei gloated.

"They probably got too tired of arguing with you all the time." Slavic retorted shortly. He turned over.

"Well, look who's talking!" Alexei said angrily. "I guess you never argue!"

"Not like you do. I keep quiet until they give in, but you argue all the time. I think they didn't say anything today because they get tired of hearing you talk back to them."

Alexei was furious. How dare Slavic talk like this? He, too, had said that he was too sick to go to church this morning!

He jumped up and began pulling his shirt on. He pushed his brother rudely before he went out the door into the summer sunshine.

He looked glumly at the packed dirt in the courtyard. All was silent except for the goat in her pen. His mother would probably take her out this afternoon. It was now three years since he had told his mother he was too busy to take care of the goat. She uncomplainingly took over.

Alexei kicked at a stone. It skittered across the yard and hit the wooden fence on the far side. He sat on the concrete stoop and sat brooding in the sun.

Things were no better. His father still tried to keep the family alive by working odd jobs. No one was allowed to give him regular employment. The kolhoz workers at least had plenty of food to eat. They all made sure of that because when evening came, their sacks were well loaded with grain and vegetables for their families. The farm director turned a sightless eye to all the plundering. Everyone did it. After all, they were constantly told that everything belonged to the people. That was the communist way. And they were the people. It was that simple.

Alexei knew that even if his father had worked on the collective farm, he still would not have brought food home. His father said that was stealing. And his father would never steal. God would be displeased.

Shaking his head, Alexei tried to reason it out. It made no sense. His parents continually said they trusted in the Lord to look after them and yet they continually lived in poverty. They barely had enough to eat, wore worn-out clothes, and never knew if they could survive another winter. It was enough to weary anybody, Alexei thought.

More and more, he was becoming convinced that he would try another way. Some way to escape the poverty they were in.

He knew his family was not the only poor family in the village. The other people who gathered in homes for Sunday worship were no better off than they. Some were even worse off. Take *Lubov Timofeyevna* for example. Her husband was in prison because he was the pastor of the church, and now she was left to fend for herself. Alexei knew his parents often carried food from their own meager store to help the unfortunate woman.

"Hello!" A voice called out from beside the yard gate.

Alexei stared at the man. He was well-dressed and looked out of place in this dusty village. Especially at their gate.

"Hello!" he called again.

Alexei stood up. He looked dumbly at the stranger.

"Are your parents at home?"

Alexei shook his head. Then he found his tongue. "What do you want?"

"I am a journalist. I came to speak with your parents for an interview."

"An interview? They are not here. They are at church." Alexei answered. A real, live journalist! Wow!

"Who are you?" the stranger asked in a friendly tone.

"I am Alexei. I live here."

"Maybe you can answer some of my questions," the journalist smiled at the teenage boy.

"Yes! Come in!" Alexei opened the gate. He liked this friendly man.

For over an hour, the journalist asked questions. He scribbled quickly as Alexei told him about their family.

"Your father and mother believe in God, don't they?" Alexei could hear the tinge of scorn in the journalist's voice.

"Yes," Alexei said, blushing. "But I don't!"

At this, the journalist raised his right eyebrow. "What do you believe in?" His pen made little scratchy sounds as he wrote rapidly.

"I believe in nothing," Alexei said proudly. "I am going to escape this poverty we live in and do something to make money. I want to become an educated person. Perhaps I will become a scientist, or—or even a writer!"

He looked eagerly at his visitor. He was ready to share his dreams with this man. This man would understand Alexei's ambitions.

But for some reason, the journalist did not seem impressed. He seemed more interested in his father. Mostly he seemed interested in how his father made a living for the family. He asked how much livestock they owned and when Alexei told him they only owned a goat, the journalist seemed surprised. He looked toward the goat shed.

"No chickens?" he asked as he wrote in his notebook.

"We used to have several but when we were required to give 300 eggs for our quota, we had to kill them. Otherwise, we would have been fined and accused of hiding chickens somewhere." Alexei tried to explain the dilemma that he still remembered so well. "Papa finally took 300 onions from our garden to pay our taxes. That year, we had to do without any onions at all."

The journalist sympathetically clucked his tongue and then got up from the bench. "Thank you very much for the interview." He held out his hand.

Alexei shook the proffered hand. "You are welcome. When will the article be printed?"

"I don't know. Keep looking for it."

Alexei did.

"How could he have written this stuff! Lies! That's what it is! '. . . evident that the pastor is well-paid for the illegal activities he conducts in the church. Suitcases of money were carried in after the parents came home from what they called their church services.' He wasn't even here when you came home from church!" Alexei crumpled the newspaper and threw it away from him in disgust.

"Alexei," his father said, "remember when I told you earlier that newspaper reporters write what they are instructed to write? They are not free to write what they know and see."

"But such outright lies! He wrote things I never said and he writes it as though he's quoting my exact words. He even wrote that I am a believer like you are! I plainly told him that I live my own life and that I do NOT believe like you do!"

Alexei went to school, disgusted with life. For years now he had been looking to educate himself out of the poverty his parents lived in. He was tired of living like they. He had thought that somehow the ideals that were taught in school could liberate him, and the journalist had seemed to embody those ideals and what education could bring Alexei.

Now this. Another disappointment.

"Alexei, you are a fine young man of seventeen. You are doing well in school. Our best teachers have done an excellent job in instructing you. With the high marks you are receiving in mathematics, you will be able to advance rapidly and get a wonderful job!" The director of the school smiled broadly at Alexei.

Something was up. Alexei knew that. The director did not call him into his office just to tell him that he was doing well in school.

"However, there is one little problem that we should address. You never signed up with the Komsomol and that has hindered many of your advancements. Now, I understand that your parents have had a big influence in your life and what they say means a lot to you. But, surely you understand that they have not had the education you are getting, and that they do not understand the great advances of science.

"It is time that you make up your own mind. You need to choose to serve the Party and become an active member. You need to give up your childish ideas about God."

Alexei looked straight into the director's eyes. "I do not believe what my parents believe. I live my own life."

"Good, good." The director was silent for a moment. Then he spoke again. "But it is written here that you said you are a believer."

Alexei looked to where the director was pointing. The newspaper!

"That is not true! I told the journalist that I am not a believer! He lied when he wrote that!"

The director sprang to his feet. "I will let you tell him then! For here," he swung open a door leading into another office, "is the journalist!"

"Well, well! We meet again, young friend!" The journalist came forward with a warm smile, hand outstretched toward Alexei.

Alexei stood rigidly, hands at his sides. Then deliberately, he put his hands behind his back. "I will not shake the hands of a liar!"

The journalist's face flushed a deep red. He dropped his hand and looked nervously at the director.

"Alexei!" There was a menacing tone in the director's voice. "You have overstepped all decency. Apologize for what you just said."

"I will not apologize," Alexei stated boldly. "He wrote lies in the newspaper about my parents. He wrote lies about me. A person who writes lies is a liar."

"You are dismissed!" the director yelled. "Get out of my office, you—you—believer!" he spat the word at Alexei in disgust.

"Where is everybody?" Alexei wondered out loud to himself. He paced the tiny front room of his parents' home. Once more, he looked out the window toward the street.

His parents had left for church again, without him. He hardly ever accompanied them anymore.

"Sunday sickness," his father called it. By now, Alexei knew his parents were no longer referring to his physical health when they called it that, but to his spiritual health. He tried to shove those thoughts aside.

Again, Alexei looked outside to see if his friends were coming. He had told them that the house would be empty and they could play cards for hours if they came. Perhaps they would bring some vodka. Then they could really party.

He began pacing the room again. Passing a small table, he saw a brochure lying there. THE TWO WAYS. The title stared at him boldly. Alexei picked it up.

He opened the tract. Standing in the middle of the room, he began to read.

It told a story of twin boys. The two did everything together. They played together, studied together, slept together, and went to school together. They also went to church together.

As Alexei read, he saw many parallels to his own life. Poverty, difficulties because of their believing parents' faith, and the tug of the atheistic school teachers on the twins' lives.

Alexei read on. The twins grew into strong young men, ready to face the world.

But something happened to the one twin. He repented. He knelt and cried out to God, and God saved him. At least, that was what the brochure said.

Deep within, Alexei felt something stir. He had seen people repent. He knew how it went. They prayed. They cried. Then, they got baptized and went to church regularly. After that, persecution started. He knew all about that.

Alexei sat down on the cot. He continued to read.

The other twin did not repent. He lived his own life and accepted the teachers' rhetoric as truth.

A chasm opened between the twins. No longer did they spend much time together. While the one went to church, the other went to parties. When Alexei read this, he shifted on the cot.

Attending parties was one thing, but the gang of boys the twin ran around with got into worse things. Things like breaking into stores, and stealing merchandise.

One day, they got caught . . . and put in jail.

As the story went on, Alexei pictured the parents and the Christian twin going to jail, trying to gain admittance. They were turned away. They were not allowed to see him until his trial.

But the first twin did not give up. Even after his parents had left, he hung around the prison. He talked to the guard and begged him to let him see his brother for just five minutes.

The guard was not willing at first, but he saw the anguish and grief that the boy was going through, so he consented. But only for five minutes, he warned!

Five minutes later, the twin came out. The guard was satisfied. His superiors would never know.

The twin went home to his parents. He went to bed. But he could not sleep. There was something heavy on his mind. A weight on his chest. On his spirit.

He began to weep. His sobs brought his parents to his room. Finding their son on his knees, crying bitterly, they joined him, mingling their tears with his.

Then the scene unfolded. This was the wrong son! The wrong twin!

The sobbing son told the story. His twin brother had come into jail to visit and told him to quickly exchange clothes with him, and then leave. They had changed places.

Alexei read on. His eyes skimmed across the page.

"He loved me so much that he took my place!" The words jumped out at Alexei as he read the anguished cry of the sobbing twin.

The rest of the story seemed unreal. As the guilty twin tried to convince the guard of the mistake, he was pushed aside. No one would believe him except his parents. No one else could comprehend that anyone would do such a thing, not even for a twin brother.

The innocent twin was tried and condemned to hard labor in prison.

The guilty twin was devastated. He could not bear his burden.

At long last, he cried out in desperation to God. Weeping bitterly, he repented of his sins.

Alexei read the story with a pounding heart. He read the analogy the author referred to at the end of the story. " 'He loved me so much that he took my place!' That is what Jesus did for us," the author said. "When we understand that great love, we will repent!"

Alexei stared into space. His breath became faster. A tear rolled down his cheek.

He brushed it away. He had not cried since he was a young boy.

"He loved me so much, He took my place!" Those words would not leave him. They cut like a knife, deep into his heart.

All his frustrations, his dashed hopes for his life, his disappointments and his unhappiness rolled together into a hard knot. His chest began to heave.

Now, tears were rolling down both cheeks. He turned his head sideways, and viciously wiped the unaccustomed wetness away. He did not want to cry.

Something was happening to him that he did not understand. It was as though he was being squeezed between giant rollers. He opened his mouth to breathe easier.

Suddenly, he remembered something.

About six months ago, after his disappointment in school, he had prayed one night. Deep in despair, he had honestly told God, "If you exist, I want a sign from you. Make me cry." He never cried. So, he thought that would be a hard test for God, if He existed.

But nothing had happened, and Alexei had not given much thought to it since.

Now this. He could not stop the flow of tears streaming from his eyes. He stumbled to his feet.

What if his friends came and found him like this? Alexei panicked at the thought.

Running across the courtyard, he dashed into the goat shed. Throwing himself on the loose hay, he began to weep in earnest.

Great heaving sobs wrenched his body. Tears coursed steadily down his cheeks and into the prickly hay.

Images of his past floated before him. He saw himself angry, defiant, and disrespectful to his loving parents. He saw himself brash, bold, tough, and indifferent to the feelings of his friends. He saw himself as a wretched creature.

Groaning, he tried to bury himself in the hay. He continued to cry. His face was wet. His chest hurt.

Alexei did not know when he began to pray. At first, he was not even aware that he was praying. He was only talking. Talking to God.

"I'm so tired of not knowing what is truth. I'm tired of feeling wretched and miserable. I'm tired of being selfish and unloving."

On and on he talked. He told the Lord about all his ambitions, his desires to make something out of himself, to lift himself out of the poverty of his parents' home. He told the Lord everything.

When he was finished and there was nothing more to say, he lay still on the hay. His body sagged against the comforting goat fodder, utterly drained. His eyes no longer shed tears. They couldn't. He had no more strength to cry.

"He loved me so much, He took my place!" The words came back to Alexei. Not loud, not demanding, but soft. Soft and loving.

Like a healing balm, they beckoned to the miserable boy. Alexei lay still, listening to the echo.

Yes. Jesus loved him. Loved the miserable wretch that he was. Loved him enough to take his place on the cross. Died for him!

The wonder that flooded his heart, his soul, his every emotion, was like a birth! Jesus loved him, Alexei, that much! Was it possible?

"I love You, too!" Alexei said the words passionately. He sat up and lifted his arms toward heaven. "Jesus! I love You, too! Oh! I love You with all my heart! I give my life to You!"

Words of praise and joy swelled up as the wonder of the love and forgiveness of Jesus washed over his soul.

New tears began to flow. This time, they were tears of joy!

For Alexei, time stopped. He did not know that he had been in the goat shed for hours. When he finally heard the yard gate open, he realized with a jolt that his parents were home from church.

With a bound, he was on his feet.

"Mama! Papa! Something wonderful happened!" He ran across the yard, and flinging his strong arms around his parents, he hugged them.

At first, his parents were astonished beyond words. Then, they understood.

"My son! Oh, my son!" Papa's words were choked with tears as he reached for Alexei. His son had found Jesus!

5

Take the Gun!

Stories of drafted men under pressure to bear arms continually surface. In this story, I interviewed the man who was told that his friend had consented to the demands of the army. He spoke eloquently of having to choose the right way for himself.

The group of twenty-some recruits were dressed in their new fatigues. Raw, bewildered, and apprehensive, they stood in a bunch like a flock of sheep. The commander, facing his new charges, eyed them critically.

"Line up!"

Stepping briskly and smartly, the recruits tried to remember the shouted instructions.

"Shoulders back! Chins in!"

Backs stiffened even more.

"Shoulders back!" the commander screamed. His voice filled the courtyard.

Chests protruded as the drafted boys struggled to get into the unaccustomed posture.

"Hah! You infants have much to learn!" He turned and barked a command. A lieutenant stepped forward and stood beside a case of rifles.

"*Florescu Lucian,* come forward and take your gun!"

The time had come. *Ioan* swallowed hard and forced himself to keep his gaze straight forward. Suddenly, in spite of the early winter chill, he felt hot all over.

"*Casian Dorin!*"

The commander called name after name. Each time, the recruit stepped forward, received a rifle from the lieutenant, and stepped back into line.

Out of the corner of his eye, Ioan saw his friend *Nelu* shift slightly.

"Give me the courage I need, oh Lord," Ioan prayed desperately. "Make me strong for Jesus' sake."

"*Lenucu* Nelu!"

Nelu stepped forward. Unhesitatingly, he walked up to stand in front of the lieutenant. But when the rifle was proffered, Nelu did not take the gun. Instead, he said in a calm voice, "I will not bear arms. I will not use weapons to kill."

The lieutenant glared contemptuously at Nelu. It had been quiet before, but now there was absolutely no noise. All eyes were fixed on the commanding officer.

"What nonsense!" A stream of profanity spilled out into the silence. The commander strode forward toward the two men and grabbed the rifle. He took the stock and pushed it into Nelu's limp hand. He grabbed Nelu's right arm and tried to get him to wrap his fingers around the barrel.

Nelu looked straight into the officer's eyes. "Sir," he said respectfully, "I will not bear arms. I will be firm in my convictions."

"Quiet!" roared the enraged man. "Get over there to the side! I will deal with you later!"

"*Feraru Gheorghe!*"

The next boy marched forward, took his gun, and returned to the line.

Ioan tried desperately to quiet his beating heart. He glanced over at his friend.

Nelu was standing quietly to one side of the group. His shoulders were back, his eyes straight forward, and no sign of emotion showed on his youthful face.

"*Macovei* Ioan!"

Ioan felt himself respond. He tried to step up bravely as he had seen Nelu do. He forced his wobbly legs to move forward.

The polished wooden stock of the gun was thrust toward him.

The metal barrel shone.

"I will not bear arms." Ioan was surprised at his own voice. It came out, clear and steady.

He saw contempt and disgust in the lieutenant's face. He steeled himself for the wrath of the commander.

There were no words. All was silent. Ominously silent.

Ioan kept his eyes straight forward, looking at the outstretched arm pushing the rifle toward him. He could actually hear his heart thudding loudly in his chest.

"So, another one." The commander spoke calmly, without feeling.

At first, Ioan was surprised. He had expected shouting, cursing, and a tirade of humiliating words. Instead, he heard only the simple words: "So, another one."

"Step aside. We will deal with you later."

It took only several more minutes for the rest of the recruits to get their guns, but for Ioan, it was a long time. His legs twitched. His nose itched. And for some reason, his hands felt empty. He had nothing to hold on to, nothing to grasp. Only empty hands.

All the other recruits now had their hands filled . . . with rifle butts.

Ioan felt the humiliation of being singled out and displayed. He could feel the eyes of the other boys boring into him. Whenever the commander spoke, he used a different tone, a sinister snarl that sent chills through Ioan.

All during the drill, Ioan was ignored. He could hear the maneuvers of the soldiers as they were instructed on how to properly hold their guns, how to salute, and how to stand "at ease." The shuffle of feet and the brush of sleeves, as the guns changed positions, all came clearly to Ioan as he stood, still facing forward, staring at a concrete wall.

He was scared. Scared and lonely.

"Lenucu Nelu! Follow me!"

Ahh! Nelu! All at once, warmth swept over Ioan. He was not alone! In his anxiety, he had forgotten about his friend! Comfort settled around Ioan's heart as he remembered Nelu's clear, calm words. "I will not bear arms. I will be firm in my convictions."

"Macovei Ioan!"

The room where Ioan was taken was empty except for a desk and a chair behind the desk. The door was locked behind him, and he heard the lieutenant's footsteps fade away down the hall.

He did not have to wait long. A key turned in the lock, and the door swung open quickly. A uniformed man Ioan had not seen before entered purposefully.

Ioan watched as the officer marched around the desk, pulled out the chair, and sat down. He stared at Ioan, then looked at a file in his hands.

"So you are one of the stupid men who refuse to take a rifle," the officer said. "You know what will happen if you refuse to bear arms. You will be tried in court and sentenced to prison."

Ioan gathered up courage and replied, "Yes, I know. I have heard how my brethren have suffered because they were not willing to carry a gun . . . to kill."

"And what would happen to our country, to Romania, if everyone would take this kind of attitude? Who would defend our homeland?"

Ioan was silent for a moment as he tried to think of how to answer. "I believe that God would take care of Romania if everyone trusted in Him."

"God!" the officer snorted in exasperation. "There is no God! We are intelligent, educated people and we need to put away all such weak, foolish ideas of God! That is for ignorant, simple old women! Not for young men like you!"

Ioan tried again. "I must be true to my conscience. I cannot go against what I know is right."

"Conscience! You—a young man who has hardly lived! What do you know about a conscience?"

Ioan blinked. "I know that I will try to be true to my conscience. I will not go against it."

"Hah! That's what you think! Wait until we are finished with you! You will not even remember that you have a conscience! You will find out that if you are hungry enough, long enough, you would eat your own parents in order to survive!"

"No!" Ioan gasped out hoarsely. "I have something different! Something you do not understand! My faith in God will take me through anything!"

"Brave words, young man. Brave words! We will see!"

———————————

"So, how is the brave young man this morning? After spending a night in that black, stinking hole all by yourself, you are surely ready to reconsider and take your rightful place with the rest of your division. The soldier's barracks are not exactly like home, but I know you will realize they are much better than the place where you spent last night!"

Ioan faced the same officer who had spoken with him the day before. He fought to think clearly in spite of the weariness that seeped through him.

"You may as well give up now. You can only last several days anyway. By the third day you will be too hungry to think of anything but food. Nobody lasts longer than four days. They all give in."

Ioan knew this was not true. He remembered the testimonies of other believers who had been released after their prison sentences were over. They had not given in. Nor would he.

"I will not bear arms." It strengthened his faith to hear his own voice speak the words. "I will be true to what my conscience tells me is right."

The officer did not try much longer to convince him to join his regiment. He called for a guard, and Ioan was once again escorted to his cell.

There, locked in the tiny, cold cell, Ioan prayed. He poured out his heart to God, pleading for strength to endure whatever he might have to suffer.

He tried to sleep. He had not slept the night before.

His feet were so cold they felt numb. The numbness crept up his legs. Ioan shivered uncontrollably.

Walking back and forth in his confining cell, Ioan tried to keep the circulation moving in his legs. He felt weak and faint from hunger. His body cried out for rest, for sleep.

If he dozed off for even a moment, it was always the cold that awoke him. In desperation, he pulled his arms inside his coat and let the sleeves dangle. His teeth chattered.

The hours stretched on and on. He was left completely, utterly alone. No one, not even a guard, interrupted his silent vigil. Ioan wondered how long he would be left here all by himself.

Perhaps he would be left here, forgotten, until he died. He tried to imagine what form death would take if it came for him in this cell.

Would he be lucid? When hunger or cold finally finished him off, would he still be conscious the last few moments? Would he be able to sense that his time of leaving this world would be near?

Ioan sat on the metal bunk and wrapped his arms around his legs, trying to gather heat from his own body. The cold crept in yet closer.

Suddenly through the bars, down the corridor, came the sound of music! A man's voice was singing—singing some words over and over. Not loudly, but clearly.

Ioan strained to hear. He got up and walked over to the bars. He put his face as close to the cold metal as he dared, and listened.

Yes, from far away, he could hear snatches of a song. ". . . You lift me up when I am sad . . . When it is dark, You make me glad."

The voice rose and fell as it came wafting through the corridor.

It was Nelu! Ioan felt sure it was!

He had often heard Nelu sing. In church, walking through the woods, or anywhere he felt he had the freedom to sing, Nelu sang.

Dear Nelu! What a comfort he was to Ioan. Never could he ask for a dearer friend.

Ioan tried to huddle into a comfortable position on his bunk. "Thank You, God, for allowing me to hear Nelu's song! I know that I am not the only one who is suffering. If he can sing, I can sing!"

Ioan sang. He sang all the songs he could think of, then started over. He sang until his voice got hoarse.

It helped. The cold seemed less severe, the hunger less keen. By faith, Ioan claimed the promises of God he was singing about. He knew that the Lord was with him.

"Take the gun! If you let it fall, I will punish you severely!" The officer forced the rifle into Ioan's hands.

Ioan kept his arms limp. The officer had taken Ioan's hands, placed the gun in them, and curved his own hands around Ioan's.

Slowly, the officer released his own hands. The gun began to slide through Ioan's hands toward the floor.

"Hold the gun!" The words came out loudly, strong and forceful.

Praying silently, Ioan continued to let the rifle slide.

At the last possible moment, the officer grabbed the gun. Reversing the rifle so its stock was turned toward Ioan, he struck the young man on the shoulder.

Ioan winced in pain as the heavy wooden rifle crashed into him.

"I will make you take this gun," the officer said through clenched teeth. He began beating Ioan on his back, again and again. Ioan tried not to cry out. He tried to be brave. Tears rushed from his eyes with each blow.

"You will bear arms!" the officer spat. "If not today, you will by the time I'm finished with you!" Then he gave Ioan a vicious shove, pushing him violently against the wall. "Take him back to his cell."

This was the first time Ioan had been struck. It was clear that the officer's patience was wearing thin. But Ioan's resolve to stay true to his convictions did not waver. Constantly, he thought of others who had suffered for their faith and remained steadfast. Simply knowing that somewhere Nelu was enduring the same persecution made it easier. He remembered that miserable night in prison when he had heard Nelu singing. More than once, that memory alone brought a deep joy into his heart.

Day after day, for a whole week, the officer tried to coerce Ioan into taking the rifle. One day, he tied Ioan's hands to the gun so that he had no choice but to hold it. Ioan tried to move his hands inside the tight cords that bound him, but he couldn't.

"Now, you have held the gun in your hands. You may as well give up this stupid struggle with your conscience. You have already done it, regardless of what you want to do. This fact can never be erased from your memory. You are bearing arms." The officer laughed a diabolical laugh. "I have won this fight!"

Ioan stood passively, the gun drifting away from him at a crazy angle. The officer pushed it upright over Ioan's shoulder.

"Don't you know that Lenucu Nelu tried that exact same resistance before he gave up and took the gun? You are not so smart in trying to think of ways to get out of the army. Lenucu was just as stubborn, but we convinced him in the end."

Ioan looked quickly into the officer's eyes. He tried to read the truth in the hard stare that met him. Had Nelu given up?

No, Nelu wouldn't give up. He relaxed. It was he who had been very instrumental in Ioan's conversion. It had been Nelu's sincerity that had impressed Ioan with a desire to live a different life, to have something better for himself. No, Nelu would not have given up.

The officer continued to stare intently at Ioan. A gleam of interest showed that he was intently watching Ioan's reaction.

The very next day, when Ioan was again sent into the office, he saw the same man at his desk. The officer was reading a file so Ioan waited at the door.

"Lenucu reported for duty on November 11, 1977." He seemed oblivious to Ioan's presence. Muttering to himself, he began to write. "Realizing his duty to his country and recognizing his error, Lenucu has successfully been reinstated with his division."

Ioan listened in dismay. Deep inside, he felt some of his strength and resistance begin to shrivel as he watched the commander write. Listening to the half-muttered report about his friend made him cold all over.

"Lenucu has signed a statement renouncing all earlier scruples against being an active soldier, and is willing to do his civic duty. I am hereby signing this statement as his commanding officer to rescind any and all sentences against Soldier Lenucu. He is to be totally forgiven in acknowledgment of his allegiance to our great country of Romania." The commander stopped writing and paused with his pen held in midair.

"Oh! Macovei! You are here!" The commander looked up from his paper work. "I have had good news!

"Your friend Nelu Lenucu has written and signed a statement that he is now willing to bear arms and take his place with the rest of his division. I have pardoned him from having to carry out his prison sentence, and he is now practicing in the field with the rest.

This is good news and we are proud of his compliance."

Ioan could not speak. He scanned the room. Yesterday, there had been two rifles leaning against the wall in the corner. Today, there was just one. Just his.

His thoughts churned wildly. What had caused Nelu to give up? Had he finally relented because of the persuasion of the commander? Had he grown weary of the frigid isolation cell, the bread and water diet, the cruel beatings and mocking? How could he have given up? He had been the strong Christian and Ioan had depended on him to lead the way. Was it possible?

The commander was talking, almost kindly. "Just take the gun and practice. You probably will never have to actually shoot someone anyway. Most of our soldiers serve their two years and never fire a shot at anyone. Our country is at peace, not at war. You can be true to your conscience and still be a good soldier. Many have done it. There is no need to go through suffering just to listen to some whim. After all, you need to be a good citizen and help make our country great. *Ceausescu* is depending on all of you young men. We will be a great country! We will be a world power! *The* world power!"

The flow of words washed through Ioan's consciousness. He heard the words, yet he did not hear them. In his weakened state, only one searing thought burned in his mind. Nelu had given up! Nelu was now out there with the other soldiers, training on the field. No more lonely, freezing nights in the cell for him, no more starvation rations, no more beatings, no more harassments. He looked at the gun.

The commander saw his glance. He stopped talking. His eyes darted from Ioan's face to the gun and then back again.

All was silent.

"I will make it easy for you. I will write here that you are willing to go into training. All you have to do is sign your name." The officer's voice was firm, yet kind. He began to write.

As the pen rolled across the paper, Ioan watched breathlessly.

"*Sign!*" a voice whispered in his ear. "*Nelu did, and many others before him. You can be a good soldier and still be true to your conscience! If you would ever have to shoot, you could intentionally miss! Sign and you will be treated like a human being again!*

You will have food! A warm place to sleep! A good life!"

"Come, Macovei! Sign right here and I will take you to the dining hall for some good hot soup. Then we will go out and join the others. Join Lenucu! He signed!" The officer thrust the pen forward, inviting Ioan to sign the statement.

Something else began to stir in Ioan's mind. For some reason, he felt as though he had been in this situation before. He remembered having to make a momentous decision once before in his life. It was uncanny how similar the situation seemed to be.

Ahh! Yes! It was the night he had wrestled with giving his life to Jesus!

So many "good" reasons why he should resist the Holy Spirit had come to him. He had known he would need to give up many of his old pleasures if he should make the choice to follow Christ.

But in the end, it had been Jesus' love for him that had won the battle. Ioan now clearly remembered how he had felt the love of Christ for his sinful soul sweep through him. How wonderful it had felt afterward to rest in that love!

It was still wonderful! That thought swept through him again. The officer was waiting, still offering the pen. But a supernatural strength flooded Ioan's being and he heard himself speak.

"No! I will not sign. I cannot sign, even if others signed. Even if Nelu signed!" He repeated, "I won't, even if he did!

"I cannot deny my Savior who gave His life for me! He is my Friend, the One who loved me even while I was a sinner. Never will I deny Him. I will take whatever punishment you give me, but I will never sign. I am ready to suffer even until death for my Lord, my Savior!" The torrent of words poured out of his soul.

The commander stared at the transformed young man. He realized his cause was lost.

Throwing the pen on the desk, he jerked open a drawer. He slid his hand in the drawer and, with a smooth motion, withdrew a pistol. In a barely controlled rage, he came around the desk and walked up to Ioan.

"I will blow your brains out!" he snarled, holding the pistol only a few inches from Ioan's temple.

"Pick . . . up . . . that . . . pen! Sign!" He bit out each word, slowly and distinctly.

"No!" Ioan did not hesitate. "I am willing to die for my Jesus!" He spoke quietly. He was ready and resigned. Nothing would budge him.

Time froze. He closed his eyes. The pistol touching his temple did not move away. The officer's forefinger still curled around the trigger meant death. Ioan waited.

Death—but not eternal death. To Ioan, it would be life! Eternal life! Life with Jesus!

At that moment, Ioan realized that no one else could make the choice for him. He had to stand on his own faith in God. Nelu could not make the choice for him. He, himself, had to make his own decision.

He *had* made the crucial decision! And because of God's love, he had taken that final stand. And if need be, he would die for his faith! If need be.

But there was no shot. No tearing explosion in the side of his face.

Ioan opened his eyes. The officer had dropped his arm and was staring at him. Ioan saw respect, and, yes, even admiration reflected there.

"You will not give up." The statement was spoken without anger, without rancor. The anger had completely drained from the officer's voice. "Such dedication I wish for all of my soldiers. Even with training, many are not loyal when they face death. Many turn into cowards and try to run."

For a month longer, Ioan was subjected to harassment, persecution, and coercion. But the trials were no longer a severe testing for him. Each time, he used the opportunity to speak boldly for the Lord. He was not only willing to suffer for his faith, he was also glad he could be a witness of what God had done in his life.

Sometimes the officer seemed to listen, and other times it made him angry. But Ioan did not give up. In fact, he almost looked forward to the daily interrogations.

After his court-martial, he was not surprised to see his friend Nelu in the automobile factory, doing forced labor. Ioan had long ago realized that the officer had lied. Nelu had not given in and taken a gun. The lie had been used to try to break him when he, Ioan, was weakened by lack of food and rest. Nelu had never signed that paper.

For the rest of his life, Ioan would remember the trial he had faced that fateful day. It was pivotal in his Christian walk of life, for he had come to the realization that no one else could make his decision for serving the Lord. He had to make it himself. Only his personal faith in the Lord would ever be able to sustain him in times of stress. Others could help him, encourage him, and influence him, but his vibrant testimony was that only Christ could truly help him. Only God was his very present help in time of trouble.

6

"My Son! My Son!"

What can compare with a Christian father's desire to know that all is well with his son's soul? Finding rest under duress is possible only by our faith in Jesus Christ and allowing God to take care of the things we cannot control. When God spoke by shaking the earth in March 1977, miracles took place.

The time has come. For a long time, we have known what lies ahead of us. Every time I notice *Beniamin's* shoulders broadening, his face filling out, and his physique maturing, I am filled with an inner dread of what he will soon have to face.

You see, in Romania, as in many other countries, all young men must report for military duty when they reach the age of twenty-one. For years it has been this way. But I think that now, during the rule of *Ceausescu*, it is the hardest for our people. Anyone who refuses to bear arms is subjected to long years in prison, extreme working conditions, torture, and at times even death.

I endured it, too, some thirty years ago, when I refused to bear arms when called up. I was sentenced to hard labor for twelve years. I still remember how relieved I was when a judge reduced my sentence to six years "because he is lacking in intelligence." Even though it was a disgrace to be considered mentally deficient, I was glad for the reprieve.

That was then. This is now. Once more, we face the threat. Only this time, it is not I, but our son.

Beniamin is the oldest in our family of nine. As I said, we have seen him maturing, both physically and mentally, but most of all spiritually. We have been trying to prepare him for this time. The time when he would be called into the army.

Now, the letter has come. He is to report to the army office on Monday. Today is Friday.

Beniamin left today. Oh, how my heart ached to see him leave! As we knelt in a circle for a final prayer, I thought my heart would break. Nothing has prepared me for this feeling of pain. I thought Beniamin would need to be strengthened and encouraged for the coming ordeal, yet it was I who was weakest. Even my wife seemed to bear up better than I. I bottled up my true feelings as best as I could.

"Good-bye, Mama. Good-bye, *Tata*. I know you will continue to pray for me. Pray not only that I may be strong to bear whatever hardship I might have to bear, but pray, too, that I can tell others about Jesus my Savior!" Beniamin's words ring in my heart. They were his final words before he turned and left for the bus.

Our entire family stood in the doorway, waving to him. I think we were all crying.

Later, by myself in the cow barn, I allowed my emotions to pour forth. In anguish, I began to weep. I remember so well my own interrogations, the mocking and cruel punishment I received during my time with the army. I remember the scorn and disgust the officers showed when they spoke to me. Now, my son is facing the same thing. How can I bear it? Gladly, would I take his place.

Tonight, the pain is still here. I find myself hurting in a way that I never knew possible. My faith in God is the only thing that sustains me. I know God is able to give Beniamin all the strength he needs, just when he needs it. But I still grieve and hurt for what my son must endure.

It is now three months since Beniamin left. Yesterday we received a letter from the court that he is to be tried for "insubordination" to the State. Although it may be a trap, *Magda* and I have actually been invited to witness the trial of our son. So, today, we are journeying by train to attend the court session tomorrow.

"You are Beniamin *Braza's* parents?" an officer came forward as soon as we walked through the gates of the courtroom compound early this morning.

"Yes," I responded.

"Come this way." He turned and, with his companion on the other side of us, we went around the courthouse and approached a wing of the great building. We mounted several steps onto a small covered porch. A locked metal door barred the entrance.

"Step up here," the officer pointed to a small platform. With a wave of his hand, he then pointed to a small window, barely large enough to frame my head.

I stepped up to the window with Magda close behind me. We peered inside.

"Beniamin!" I cried out. My voice cracked and sudden tears blurred my vision.

"Tata! You are here!" I could hear the surprise in his voice. "Mama, too! Praise God!"

"Son! How are you? Are you trusting the Lord?" I cried out hoarsely.

"Oh, Tata! God is so good! He has been so real to me! When I am tried, when I am hurting, or simply when I get discouraged, He sends comfort through His Spirit. Tata, God is wonderful!"

As my eyes adjusted to the gloomy room he was waiting in, I could see the handcuffs that bound his arms together at the wrists. I winced, looked away, then looked back at Beniamin again. "God bless you, my son! 'Blessed are ye, when men shall revile you, and persecute you, and shall say all manner of evil against you falsely, for my sake. Rejoice, and be exceeding glad: for so persecuted they the prophets which were before you!' " I moved away from the tiny window so Magda could look inside.

"Beniamin! Be strong in the Lord and put all your trust in Him!" My wife spoke clearly and encouragingly. "Be not dismayed for what you are enduring. Be faithful to the end! We are praying for you!"

"Enough!" The officer's voice pulled us away from the window. "You must leave now!"

We turned reluctantly from the window. "Good-bye until we meet again, Beniamin! God be with you!" Magda quickly called out before we were pulled away.

"Now you saw your son. Did you like what you saw? Do you like what you have taught him?" the officer asked in a cold voice.

"Sir, what would you have liked us to teach him? We have taught him to obey God, to be true to his conscience, and to love all men."

The officer scowled. "You have not taught him to be obedient to those in authority. He has defied all our orders. He is to be tried as a criminal."

As the accusations poured out, my heart constricted. But something within gave me a boldness. "I disagree, sir. We have taught him to obey those in authority. We have never taught him to be a disobedient son. He has always, since he is grown, tried to obey his mother and me."

"Then why does he refuse to obey us? We have ordered him over and over again to take his place with the rest of his unit and, every time, he refuses. He keeps saying that he has to 'obey God rather than men' or something like that."

I did not want to argue, but I told him simply. "He is being true to his conscience. I am sure that in all other areas he is willing to obey."

"We will see how true to his conscience he will be by the time we are finished with him. No one can hold out against us forever." The officer spoke confidently.

"The same God Who gave me strength to be true to my beliefs will also give Beniamin strength," I told him. "I will pray that he will be faithful."

"You!" There was contempt in his voice as the officer looked at me disdainfully. "You do not know what you are talking about."

Magda's voice broke the silence. "Yes, sir, he does. My husband suffered for six years for his faith in God. You see, we are ready to suffer, even die, for our faith. God is always with us."

The officer glanced sharply at me. "Go! You are dismissed."

Magda and I walked around the courthouse to the front. Soldiers in uniform were pouring into the courthouse. Hundreds of them were inching their way inside.

When we joined the press and worked our way toward the door, a guard blocked the way. "You cannot come in!" he said peremptorily and pushed us away.

"We have permission. Our son is inside." I protested.

"Who gave you permission?" he barked.

I unfolded the letter we had received. He read it, then motioned us inside.

The huge courtroom was filled to capacity. Most of the audience was made up of soldiers.

The trial started. "Bring the accused in," the judge ordered.

A side door opened, and immediately I saw Beniamin being escorted under guard toward the front. A lump formed in my throat and I felt my eyes begin to water. I brushed at my tears impatiently.

He looked so calm. No sign of stress showed on his face, but rather a deep glow seemed to shine from his countenance. He looked thin, but healthy.

Along with him, they brought two dark-skinned, black-haired boys. All three were lined up in front of the judge's bar, Beniamin in the middle. He stood a good head higher than the boys on either side of him.

Since we were at the back of the room to one side, we could see Beniamin's profile as he stood, waiting for the court to begin.

The prosecuting officer read the charges. The two Gypsies were charged as deserters, and Beniamin was charged with insubordination.

I listened keenly to what the prosecutor charged the three boys with. He made no distinction between the two charges. They were both crimes against the State, against the government, and the three boys were presented as equally criminal.

"Lord," I prayed, "give Beniamin the right words to speak. Give him the strength to be faithful to his convictions. Thank You, Lord, for what You are doing for him!" I was so proud of our son. He stood, tall and straight, and answered all his charges in a clear voice.

Time and again, he was asked why he refused to obey the government. Every time, his answer came strong and clear. "I will obey the government in all things, as long as it does not violate God's Word and my conscience."

They tried to persuade him to recant. They told him he could be reinstated with his unit if he would simply obey orders and bear arms. For several hours, they tried to convince him.

The two Gypsies were taken away. They were both condemned to death. Their wails of terror were quickly muffled by the guards as they were dragged off.

Still, they were not finished with Beniamin. Different army officials took the stand and tried to convince Beniamin to give up.

Finally, the judge intervened. "Enough!" He turned to the prosecutors. "You have tried to convince this young man to give up his faith and join his unit. You have argued for hours. All you have done makes him more convinced than ever that he is doing the right thing! I have seen him becoming stronger, while you are becoming weaker!"

The prosecuting team stood withered under the judge's scorn. They glanced nervously at each other.

The judge continued. "You look like you are the accused and he is your judge. Look at him! Does he look convinced he is wrong? Have you done anything that makes him feel guilty? No! He stands above all of us in this courtroom!"

I was amazed and yet not surprised. For it really was true. Beniamin truly was the winner. Even though he was the accused, he looked as calm and fresh as when the trial started.

"Nevertheless, I sentence Beniamin Braza to four years in prison, because he has refused to bear arms in our national army. Let this trial be a lesson to all the young men in this courtroom. You heard the sentence for the two deserters. You now hear the sentence of one who refuses to bear arms! Court dismissed!"

———————————

Magda and I are now on the train on our way home. We could be heavy-hearted and sorrowful, but for some reason we aren't. True, we are weary, but not heavy-hearted. A deep, underlying happiness radiates through us.

"Praise God. Beniamin is growing in his spirit!" Magda said joyfully a few minutes ago. "I could see it on his face!"

My heart was too full for words, but I nodded in agreement. Magda is right. The Lord is faithful in supplying our son with the grace and strength to endure his trials.

Every month, I have been allowed to visit Beniamin in prison. Magda always sends a parcel along. We know we cannot send any written material or letters in the package. They would be confiscated, of course. So, she sends food.

Everyone in Romania knows one of the worst things about our jails is the lack of food. To be in jail and not have anyone from "outside" bringing food can be a disaster. The prison food is simply awful.

Even though our food supply at home is not varied, God has always blessed us with plenty of potatoes. And, most of the time, we have bread. Occasionally, Magda butchers one of the old hens that are no longer laying, and adds bits of chicken to our soup.

From this supply, she always sets aside portions for Beniamin. None of the other children complain. We are together as a family in our desire to help him. Even the youngest, four-year-old Maria, gladly gives up her piece of bread for Beniamin.

This procedure has been working well for six months now. At our brief, ten minute visits, Beniamin and I can always visit long enough for both of us to be encouraged. Actually, there are many times that I think I benefit more from these visits than he does. He is always ready to share with me how the Lord has given him opportunity to witness to some of his fellow inmates. I know he is worked hard, but he never complains.

Even though he does not talk about his hunger, or the awful condition of the food they are given, I can tell by his eager glances at the opened parcel that he is always hungry. I say opened parcel, because a guard always inspects the package before I am allowed to take it to him.

Magda never packs anything out of the ordinary. Even if we could afford it, we know better than to send anything that the guards might fancy. So, the packages usually contain boiled potatoes, bread, and occasionally some apples.

"Tata," Beniamin told me just yesterday, on my seventh visit, "I have heard that you will not be allowed any visiting rights after this month. The officials are cracking down on all of us prisoners and our rights." His voice was still strong, in spite of the distressing news.

"Oh, Beniamin!" I protested. "How can you do without the food parcel Mama sends to you! How can it be possible for you to do all this heavy work and not get extra food!'

Beniamin smiled at me. "Tata, God will provide the strength. There are times when even now I am so tired at the end of the day that I can barely eat. Yet, the Lord has been with me and He always provides strength for the next day. God can still do miracles."

"You don't eat all your food yourself, do you?" I knew the answer. I knew who he shared his food with the other prisoners.

"There are many here who are in worse condition than I am," Beniamin said sadly. "Actually, I believe I am the most blessed of all. I have a loving family who prays for me, and I know of no one else who has that. No, I indeed am blessed above all the rest."

"Time's up!" yelled the guard.

"Good-bye, Beniamin! I will try to come next month again!" I wanted to hug my son, but the wall between us kept us from any physical contact. We have only a small space at the bottom of the glass window to speak through.

I must confess that my faith is weak. I do not think there is anything we can do about gaining visiting rights with Beniamin. For true to his prediction, this month when I went to visit him, I was denied entrance. I felt helpless.

Magda, however, does not give up so easily. She convinced me to go to the head of the prison and ask for a change of rules that would allow us to visit our son.

"No! You cannot have rights to visit your son! Policy has changed! Get out!" The head officer we had finally managed to see was scornful to the extreme. He waved us toward the door.

I say "we," for Magda accompanied me. I wanted her to, for there are times when she has a wisdom and guidance that surpasses mine, and I am always grateful for her support.

"*Vasile*," Magda said to me as soon as we were outside the building, "we cannot give up so easily! Beniamin will starve! I don't think that the policy change is at all legal! I can't imagine that all the prisoners will be denied visiting rights. Our prison system is designed to have relatives bring in food for the inmates. They know it is not as expensive for the State that way."

So, three days later, we are here in *Bucharest*. Magda and I have prayed much about this trip, for the idea has seemed doomed from the outset according to natural man's thinking. Why would *Tovarasul Popescu*, the highest official in the prison system of our area, even be interested in the plight of a young man who refuses to bear arms?

But it is not just any young man, it is our son. Our son, Beniamin. We have to do what we can for him! Our love constrains us!

We will call on Mr. Popescu this afternoon.

The six flights of stairs to Mr. Popescu's office left me slightly out of breath as I knocked on the office door.

To our surprise, an immediate "Come in" sounded from within. Breathing a prayer, I pushed the door open.

Magda and I entered the room. We stood inside the door, waiting.

"What is it that you want?" Mr. Popescu looked at us, rather in surprise, I thought.

"Sir," I said. "We have come to place a petition before you. Our son, Beniamin Braza, has a four-year prison sentence. He has now served seven months of his term. Up to this time, we have had visitation rights to our son once a month. Last week I went to take a food parcel to him and to spend my allotted ten minutes with him. I was denied my rights.

"We addressed this problem to the prison official and he denied me the visitation rights. I am now appealing to you. Could you please help us, sir?"

Sitting behind his desk in disciplined military bearing, Mr. Popescu did not look like someone who would be moved with pity for our plight. He pulled a file of papers from his desk, shuffled leisurely through them, then pulled a report from the file. Meticulously, he returned the folder to the proper place, then began reading the report.

All the while, Magda and I were standing inside the door. Tired as we were from our trip, we were not asked to sit on the wooden chairs that faced the commander's desk. I shifted from one foot to the other.

"Your son is in prison for insurrection against our country! I will not rescind the order of the prison official. You are dismissed!" He said the words with finality.

I turned to go, but Magda was not so easily dismissed. "Sir!" she broke out passionately. "You don't understand! Beniamin is doing two work quotas every day! He is already weak from hunger and he needs the food parcels that we take to him! Could he at least be allowed to receive the food parcel from my husband?" My wife was almost in tears as she made her plea.

"Mail the food parcels to him!" Mr. Popescu gave a quick reply.

"Sir, you know that he would rarely, if ever, get the food unless we hand deliver it." I looked directly at him. All three of us knew that the guards would confiscate and eat or sell all the food if we would send the parcel by post.

Mr. Popescu had the grace to shift his eyes to his desk for a moment. Then, he raised his head. "Why does your son refuse to bear arms?"

So he knew all about Beniamin's trial and imprisonment. I had suspected that he did after he had read the report.

"Beniamin refuses to bear arms because of the teachings of Christ. Jesus Christ has clearly stated that we are to love our enemies. We are to do good to those who hate us, to those who despitefully use us. These are teachings from the Bible, and Beniamin refuses to bear arms because his conscience will not allow him to train to kill anyone," I told him.

Again Mr. Popescu glanced at the report. Then he did a surprising thing. He opened a drawer from his desk, drew out a black book and placed it on his desk. To our amazement, we saw that the book was a Bible!

Mr. Popescu placed one hand on the Bible. Then he picked it up and held it so we could plainly see it. "Our State law is greater than this book. A man must be willing to lay down his conscience for the sake of our country. No, you do not have the right to visit your son."

Magda looked at me helplessly. I cleared my throat. "Sir, then we will go to a Higher Power!"

"Hah!" he spat. No longer was he polite. "To whom will you go? Will you try to take your case to America? Will you try to broadcast your position on the radio program of Free Europe and have them broadcast it to the West? I warn you, if you do that, you will never see your son again!" He was almost shouting.

"No," I tried to answer calmly. "We will go to the Highest Power that exists: God Himself."

He sneered. "Take it to Him all you want. I have yet to see Him do anything! Now, get out of my office!"

That time, we left.

Now, weary from our fruitless mission, Magda and I will go home to our waiting family. My faith is still weak.

We have taken it to the Highest Power. We, and all of the brothers and sisters in our church, have begun to pray. I shared our dilemma with the fellowship on Sunday, and felt moved to ask for volunteers to fast and pray for Beniamin.

On Sunday afternoon, more than twenty young people came to our house for prayer. We knelt and poured out our hearts to the Lord. As we interceded for Beniamin, I felt deeply moved. All of these dear young people knew Beniamin. They cried out to the Lord to deliver Beniamin from anything that would cause his faith to waver. They pled with God to give him strength to endure this added hardship.

As I saw the fervency and faith with which the prayers were offered to God, my faith was strengthened. We all felt the presence of the Lord with us.

Throughout this week, many have come to our house to pray with us. I know that many are fasting, not because they told me, but because of the fervency of their prayers. It has been a week of spiritual warfare. It has also been a week of encouragement and joy for me. God has not forgotten us.

God has spoken with a thundering voice! The earthquake that shook the southern part of Romania two days ago has demolished buildings, bridges and roads. Hundreds of people have been killed, and thousands more injured. This tragic Friday in March 1977 will not soon be forgotten. All around us, I hear people crying out that God is punishing us for our sins. People are afraid. We all wonder if more earthquakes will follow the first mighty quake, and if, perhaps, truly all Romania will soon lie in ruins.

For us Christians, it is another reminder of the brevity of our lives here on earth. And as for our family, we are most amazed that the apartment building we live in has not been damaged at all! It is one of the only buildings in our town that has not been touched. The buildings all around us were either ruined or damaged greatly. We are deeply humbled and grateful to God for having spared us. Many, many have not been so providentially cared for.

In spite of the tragedy all around us, our minds immediately went to our son in prison. We were immensely relieved and thankful to the Lord when we received word that the prison was not harmed at all by the earthquake.

We helped the earthquake victims as much as we could on Saturday. We had plenty of opportunities to take food and comfort to the stricken around us.

Today is Sunday. This morning I heard a knock at the front door. I went to answer, expecting to see someone asking for food, blankets, or some other form of help. I unlocked the door, swung it open, and there stood Mr. Popescu!

"Come in! Come in!" I said after I recovered from my shock.

It was Popescu, but it was a changed Popescu. His bearing was no longer erect and haughty. His shoulders were slumped. He had shadowy circles under his eyes.

"Sit down, sir!" I said, still somewhat flustered. "My wife will get you some tea!"

He shook his head silently. He stood in our small entrance hall, holding his cap. He looked all around him, and I could see his eyes inspecting our walls and then the ceiling. "You have not been touched by the earthquake!" He shook his head slightly and then looked directly at me.

"Tomorrow, you may visit your son!"

"Oh, thank you, sir!" Magda cried. She had come to see who our visitor was and recognized him immediately.

I reached out and shook Mr. Popescu's hand. He willingly offered his hand, and then in bewilderment said again, "Your whole apartment building has not been touched by the earthquake! Someone—it must have been God—has protected you!"

"Yes, we are so thankful to the Lord for His protection! We have not deserved this mercy, but He has spared us!" My heart rejoiced that this man, the commander of the prisons, was recognizing the mighty power of God.

"All around are ruins, yet you have not been touched!" Mr. Popescu marveled again. His bloodshot eyes took a last look at the unbelievable as he turned to leave. Suddenly he swung around and looked at us again. "Tomorrow," he repeated, "you may visit your son!"

All doors opened freely to me that Monday when I went to see Beniamin. After I gave him his food parcel, I told him all that had happened.

Together, we rejoiced in the way that God had spoken to our nation. We praised the God of heaven for being merciful to us and for restoring our visiting rights.

This time there was no time limit. No guard came after ten minutes to tell me I had to leave. We visited for a long time, had prayer together, and both felt strengthened and deeply encouraged before I finally left.

Since then, I have been able to resume my monthly visits with my beloved son. We spend much time in prayer, in singing, and in praising God. All of our church rejoices in the direct answer to our prayers.

Praise the Lord! One year and three months later, Beniamin has been released. We don't know why his sentence was shortened and we will probably never know. But we are firmly convinced it was the might and power of God who orchestrated it. He has spoken to our whole country through the earthquake, and I believe it was the message of that disastrous tremor that was the key to Beniamin's release.

And oh! It is so good to have my son Beniamin at home again!

7

No Red Tie for Me, Please!

This story illustrates the intense struggle that children from Christian families endured going to an atheistic school in the 1970s. I personally know Anya and admire her strength of character. She is the wife of Mikhail in the story Fearful of Baptism.

"When the earth cooled, millions and millions of years ago, at first there was no life on earth at all! Every form of life on earth today evolved from simple life forms. Over thousands and thousands of years, those simple life forms developed into what we recognize today as horses, sheep, trees and even people." *Anya's* teacher droned on. "But all living things came from one first little living organism."

Anya squirmed. She frowned in concentration and twisted a strand of dark hair around her finger. She looked at her classmates. Some of them were listlessly sitting at their desks, bored by the monotone of their teacher reading from her textbook. Others were listening half-heartedly, lulled by the afternoon heat of autumn.

The teacher, *Antonina Fyodorovna*, looked up from her textbook and realized that her science lesson was reaching largely uninterested ears. It was time to change tactics. She stood. "*Sveta*, go to the window and bring the plant over to my desk."

This got everybody's attention. All eyes followed *Sveta* to the window as she carefully picked up the geranium and carried it to her teacher's desk.

"If we look closely at this plant, we can see that it is alive." The teacher now had the attention she desired. "Now, look at your classmates. Are they alive too?"

The second-graders looked at each other and giggled. They nodded their heads. The teacher smiled at them.

"Are you just the same as everyone else?"

"No!" blurted out *Sasha*, an impulsive boy. "I am not like Anya, because she is a girl!"

Antonina silenced the outburst of laughter with a stern look.

"But you are all humans, right? Now, look at this plant. It doesn't look like any of you, does it? But way back, years ago, all of us came from the same first living organism. Yes, Anya?"

"Antonina Fyodorovna, what is an orga . . . organ?"

"Organ*ism*," corrected the teacher. "An organism is something living."

Anya shook her head in puzzlement. "But—but we were created by God on the sixth day! And every living thing was created at different times by God. The animals! The plants! The fish, the earth and everything! My mama told me so!"

There was a quick inhalation of breath from Antonina. "Anya! Your parents are ignorant, uneducated peasants! Do you think that what your mother tells you is more correct than what our Soviet-educated scientists have discovered about our universe? Shame on you for bringing such ignorant drivel to our scientific discussion! No more!"

Anya shriveled in her seat. The scorn in Antonina's voice humiliated her spirit. She suddenly felt very much alone.

"Now class, I want you to listen closely. For many years, foolish people have believed the tales that are written in a book called the Bible. These tales were written by people hundreds of years ago and passed on down from year to year. Scientists have now proven that these stories are not true, but myths based on some actual happenings. We are now educating ourselves away from such weak, superstitious tales." The teacher's eyes snapped as she addressed the upturned faces. "Anya is a silly girl to believe such lies. Shame on you, Anya!"

Several of the children snickered in scorn and rolled their eyes. They were not stupid like Anya! They didn't believe in such tales.

Wishing she could disappear, Anya bowed her head. Tears squeezed out of her eyes. She rubbed them away.

"Now, children, all living things have the same ancestry . . . " Antonina resumed the science lesson. But Anya could no longer listen. The vicious attack on her views left her shattered.

"Mama," Anya sobbed, "school was awful today! The teacher made fun of me when I said that God made us and the animals and all living things. She made fun of me in front of the whole class!"

Mama's loving arms encircled her little girl. She sighed. Already the conflict was raging between good and evil, between darkness and light. Already the conflict had wounded this innocent child. She held her daughter more tightly. "My dear Anya," she murmured. "I am sorry that you had trouble in school. But remember, God will bless you for speaking the truth. Even though it is hard to be made fun of in front of the whole class, you never have to feel alone. God is with you all the time.

"Come, let us kneel down and pray to the Lord about it. He understands everything and will give us strength to be faithful to Him."

Mother and daughter knelt beside the cot where Anya's little sister already lay fast asleep. Committing her daughter into the hands of the Lord not only brought comfort into Anya's trusting heart, but also brought healing into the mother-heart that ached for her child.

"Today is a great time for you!" Teacher *Svetlana Alexandrovna's* voice rang through the classroom as she addressed the large group of eighth graders. "Now that you are a part of the *Komsomol*, the communist party's organization for the training of young people, you will be given the Komsomol's red tie to wear to show your membership. Our country is made up of loyal people who have taken this training and are now doctors, scientists, astronauts, and professors. Limitless opportunities abound for everyone who studies diligently and applies themselves to the available resources of our great country!"

Anya felt the familiar sickening feeling rise up inside her stomach. She had known it was coming. She had been quite aware that one day, she would have to face this dreaded time.

Ever since her parents had become believers, they had taught their children the need of being separate from the worldly concept of citizenship. Well they knew what their children would face. They counted the cost, yet taught Anya and her siblings that to pledge allegiance to the Komsomol was in essence denying the existence of God. Most of all, they had explained, they were never to accept the symbol of denying God, the red necktie.

For Anya, the red tie was so much associated with denying God that she grew up viewing it as the equivalent to a ticket to hell. Year after year, as she progressed through the grades in school, she had seen the eighth graders receive the red emblem. Year after year, it struck new terror into her heart. She had decided that no matter what the consequences would be, she would never wear that dreaded tie.

Now the great test was here. Her mouth felt dry and she nervously licked her lips.

Teacher Svetlana went on proudly. "We have with us Comrade *Scherbak*, the director of the schools of this region, to officiate in this important event. He will speak to you about what a great honor and privilege it is to wear the tie, the symbol of our powerful Soviet country." She turned as the director walked in and all the students stood respectfully.

"Good afternoon, comrades!" the director greeted the students. "It is a great privilege to be here to oversee this important event. I am sure that all of you have looked forward to this event for a long time. Just think, every year thousands of young people all over the Soviet Union take this important step and begin identifying with the motherland." On and on he talked, lauding the system of the communists, stressing the need for complete loyalty, and warning them against the corruption of religion and capitalism.

Not for a moment could Anya relax. All through the speech she felt faint.

"Now your teacher will demonstrate how you should wear the

tie." All eyes turned to Teacher Svetlana.

"*Pioter*, take this box and distribute the ties. I will show you how you are to wear them. Come, *Natasha*, I will use you as a model."

Pioter importantly placed a tie on each of the pupil's desks. The teacher continued her demonstration.

"You drape it around your neck like this." She held up the tie in the middle then placed it around Natasha's neck. "Then you take this end, bring it under like this, then tie it in a neat knot, like this!"

There stood Natasha, smiling proudly as all the students looked at her tie, a scarlet band, draped around her neck. To Anya, it looked like blood spilling onto Natasha's blouse.

"It is time to dismiss for the day, but tomorrow, I want all of you to be wearing the tie!" Svetlana paused. For a long moment, she looked at Anya. "All of you!" she repeated. There was a note of warning, of authority, in her voice.

She tapped the dismissal bell and the students filed out in orderly rows. Anya opened her desk lid and shoved the tie inside. Then she joined the other students marching in line to the outside of the school.

That night, Anya's mother spent more time than usual praying with her daughter. "I won't wear the tie, Mother," Anya promised. "I—I don't know what will happen to me, but I've decided I will never wear the tie!"

"Well!" Svetlana Alexandrovna's voice ripped across the classroom. "I see we have a little problem this morning! Good little believer Anya has decided to be her stupid self and not wear the Komsomol tie. But what else can we expect? It goes right along with her ignorant, uneducated background." Scorn and derision dripped from the angry teacher's every word.

Anya felt the red flush spread upward from her neck and across her face. She clenched her hands into tight fists under her desk.

"Where is the tie?" Teacher Svetlana marched across the room and stood in front of Anya.

Anya reached inside the desk and handed the dreaded tie to her teacher.

"No! I will not take it! You are going to wear it." Then with a quick movement the teacher took the tie and wrapped it tightly around Anya's neck. "If you won't put it on by yourself, I will put it on for you!"

Anya was frightened. She did not resist when the tie was knotted around her neck, but cowered in her seat.

"No more of this nonsense! Everyone in my class will wear the tie! I will not tolerate disobedience of any kind."

All through the class period, Anya felt ill. She wanted to remove the tie but she quailed under the teacher's watching eye. She tried to concentrate on her work, but the tie was like a chain around her neck, weighing her down, dulling her mind. Tears welled up in her eyes, making it impossible for her to read her textbook.

When the class period was over, Anya followed the other students out of the room. As soon as she was outside the door, she reached up and untied the knot. Slipping the tie into her school bag, she took a deep breath. Fresh air! It flowed into her lungs, sharply sweet.

A schoolmate, *Marina*, watched Anya sharply. Undetected by Anya, Marina darted back into Svetlana Alexandrovna's classroom.

Repercussions followed swiftly. Scarcely had Anya settled herself in the next classroom desk, minus the tie, when she heard a commotion at the door. Teacher Svetlana swept into the room like a warship under full steam.

"Wicked, rebellious girl!" The angry spate of words washed over Anya's defenseless head. "If you won't wear our tie, which you are not worthy to wear, I will give you a tie you *can* wear!"

Anya quailed.

"Marina, get the floor cleaning rag from the hall closet." Svetlana commanded briskly.

"There!" the teacher gloated. She tied the rag around Anya's neck. "You will wear the 'tie' that belongs to your kind. If you want to be different, be different. Perhaps soon all you foolish believers will want to wear an identity rag around your necks. Then we can easily see who is foolish enough to believe in God and all that nonsense!

"Look at her!" the teacher addressed the room full of students.

"Doesn't she look smart and intelligent? But of course, she looks just like what she is."

Anya was deeply humiliated as the mocking words were flung into the room. How she longed to disappear, to run home and never come back to school again.

A burst of nervous laughter came from the rest of the students. They knew they must follow the example of their teacher or her scorn would be meted out to them, too. But many a sympathetic glance was sent Anya's way. Everyone in the class knew that Anya was one of the best students in the eighth grade. Her school work was excellent.

"No more nonsense!" Teacher Svetlana prepared to leave. "The rest of you, take an example from this. Don't get any foolish notions in your head," she threatened. She had sensed the sympathy from several in the class.

"Blessed are ye, when men shall revile you, and persecute you, and shall say all manner of evil against you falsely, for my sake." The memorized words came stealing softly into Anya's consciousness.

Yes! Anya felt the encouragement right away. She straightened her shoulders, ignoring the cleaning rag around her neck, and looked for her assignment. She would not let this interfere with her lessons. To give in to fear would be to allow Satan to strike a blow against the kingdom of heaven. No, she would bear the shame of it all for Christ.

"Praise God, dear Anya, you did the right thing!" Mama smoothed her daughter's hair with a gentle hand. "God gave you that verse to remind you of His presence, I am sure. You know I am always praying for you that you can be strong."

"Mama," Anya mourned, "I am not strong. I hate being ridiculed and made fun of. I have been mocked all my school years because I believe in God, but I have never felt such strong hatred and cruelty as I did today.

"I have wished over and over again that I did not need to go to school. I have often prayed and asked God that somehow I wouldn't have to go. Today has been the worst day of my life!" Anya lay her head against her mother's shoulder. "I know I could not go through all this if it were not for you. You always make me feel better."

"I am glad, dear. But even more, I am glad you are finding that your strength comes from God. He can give you strength even when I am not there to support you. You are learning to walk with Him!"

"Why do they want everyone to be a part of the Komsomol and to wear the tie? I can understand that the Soviet government would encourage the young people to be party members, but why do they try to force everyone to become a part of the Komsomol? It should be voluntary."

"Yes, dear, but that is not the way this government operates. They operate by force, as you well know."

"But Mama, I have determined that I will not wear the tie, for it is a symbol against believing in God. I want to be true to Him!"

Anya and her mother stood in front of the director at the Religious Affairs office. Anya's father had been denied a pass from the head of the collective farm to accompany his daughter and his wife.

The director looked piercingly at the woman standing at attention in front of him. "You are not considered a fit parent for your children. Your daughter, Anya, is showing an anti-Soviet spirit and it is evident that she is getting her instruction from you, her mother. We will not tolerate such action in our region; no, not in our country. This must be stopped!"

He paused to let his words sink in.

"Sir," Anya's mother said firmly, yet respectfully, "we do not teach our children any anti-Soviet propaganda. We teach them to be obedient to the government, to pray for the government and to be obedient to the laws of the land."

"Hah!" A woman's voice from behind them burst in. "Then why does Anya refuse to wear the red tie of the Komsomol?"

It was her teacher, Svetlana Alexandrovna! Anya recognized her voice immediately.

The teacher walked briskly around the side of the desk and stood beside the director. She faced Anya and her mother squarely. "I tell you, you are lying! For all of her school years, Anya has been disrespectful to our government. Every time we have a patriotic rally, she refuses to cooperate! Now, she refuses to join the Komsomol and wear the symbol of our government, the red tie! If that isn't anti-Soviet, what is? I ask you!"

Flushed and angry, she glared at Anya's mother and continued. "You are not a fit parent! All the rest of your children are following Anya's example! Your children will be taken away from you and placed in an orphanage!"

Anya gasped in alarm. She pressed against her mother's side.

The director had sat quietly during the teacher's tirade. He watched Anya's reaction when Svetlana threatened them.

Anya found her voice. "No!" she said passionately. "Don't do that! It will not help! I will speak to my brothers and sisters about God! I will pray every day and teach them to do the same! Even if you forcibly take us children away from our parents, we will still believe in God! We will tell everybody we meet that God is good and that He created everything!"

The director looked keenly at Anya. Still, he did not say anything.

"Do something!" the teacher stormed at the director. "Don't you see what is happening? These parents are brainwashing their children, and their influence will spread in my school! I cannot have that! This God-business must be stopped, I tell you!"

"Get out!" the director spoke suddenly. He glared at Anya and her mother. "Go!" He waved his hand at them.

Quickly, the two turned and left. They heard the teacher's voice hurling accusations against them as they exited the building.

The entire family lived in dread from day to day. They talked of fleeing, but in the end they knew that was useless. They barely had enough food to get through the winter, and there was no way anyone would help them in their flight. And anyway, where could they go?

So, they did the only thing they knew to do. They went to the Lord. Anya's father prayed long and earnestly for the children each morning before they went to school. Anya knew her parents did not just pray for them in the mornings. She felt their prayers through every long, agonizing day.

Nothing happened. Teacher Svetlana continued to humiliate Anya whenever she could. She expressed her animosity in as many ways as possible. Never an opportunity did she miss to make scathing remarks about "weak, ignorant people who believe in God."

Somehow, Anya bore up through it all. There were times when fear nearly overwhelmed her and she felt the dark clouds of doubt trying to erase her faith in God. But her parents were a constant source of strength and encouragement and she felt her fears subside.

Burying her head against the flank of their family cow, Anya hummed softly to herself. The gentle evening breeze felt cool after the heat of the summer day. With rhythmic strokes, she milked the cow.

Glancing toward the village, she saw a lone figure approaching. It was a woman.

Anya continued milking. But she frequently glanced toward the woman following the path that led past where the cow was tethered.

The woman walked slowly, looking down at her feet. It was apparent that she was not in any hurry. It appeared as though some great trouble weighed heavily on her.

Anya finished with the front quarters and began milking the back quarters. The milk squirted steadily into her pail, foaming into a white froth.

Before the walker was within speaking distance, Anya felt her heart sink. It was her former teacher! It was Svetlana Alexandrovna!

Even though Anya had been out of school for more than two years, her stomach still churned in fear when she saw this woman! She tried to shrink into a smaller shape, and pressed her head against the cow's side in desperation. Perhaps Svetlana would walk on by and not recognize her.

"It's Anya."

Anya reluctantly raised her head to acknowledge the voice greeting her.

"I would know you anywhere," Svetlana said slowly.

Anya gazed at her in amazement. Her former teacher was a different person! Her voice was different! She looked different! Something had happened.

"Anya, the brave girl. The girl who was willing to stand up for her beliefs. The girl who showed me what happens when one fights against God." It was almost as though Svetlana was talking to herself.

Focusing back on the girl in front of her, she continued. "Anya, I apologize. I am sorry for the way I treated you when you were a student in my class. I did you wrong."

Anya gazed in amazement at the speaker. She forgot to milk.

"God punished me. He punished me very hard. First, my son got sick with cancer. He died. Then, I became ill. Oh, I tell you, I have been punished! So many bad things have happened to me! Yes, I am being punished by God for what I did to you! I am sorry. Will you—can you forgive me, Anya?"

Anya rose to her feet. The forgotten milk pail was left underneath the patient cow. "I forgive you, Svetlana! I am so sorry for all the difficulties you have experienced!" She could think of nothing else to say.

"Thank you!" Svetlana almost whispered, her voice breaking. "I hope that now God will forgive me, too."

She was lost in thought for a moment. Then she looked for a long time at the girl in front of her. Her eyes took in the healthy glow of Anya's red cheeks, the clear look in her dark eyes, and the freeness of spirit resting lightly on her youthful face.

"You have become a beautiful girl," she said impulsively. "All the horrid things I have done to you have not crushed you. They have made you even more beautiful."

Anya blushed at the open praise. Then, pity welled up inside of her.

"May God bless you, Svetlana. I am glad that I met you today!"

"I didn't know you were out here when I came for my walk. I was so miserable and I had to get off by myself. Now that I have met you and asked for your forgiveness, I feel better, for some reason. Maybe I can even sleep tonight!"

It was only after Svetlana left that Anya remembered her neglected chore.

"Oh, you patient animal!" she laughed to the cow. "You didn't even stir through all this!"

She sat down and resumed her task, memories filling her mind. She reflected on the unexpected meeting that had just occurred. She prayed in thankfulness and in intercession for her former enemy.

The milking done, Anya released the cow to the pasture and started home with the fresh, creamy milk. Happiness filled her heart. She began to sing once more.

8

Are My Children Safe?

As "Maria" told me this remarkable story, she continually wiped her tears in remembrance of the anguish she had endured. This story took place in southern Romania.

"**M**ama! Where did they take *Tata*?" *Viorica's* voice came out in a whisper. She pressed her seven-year-old body against her mother.

Maria's arms instinctively tightened around Lidia, her two-year-old sitting on her lap. Four-year-old Natalia shared the lap with her little sister.

Looking deep into her oldest daughter's brown eyes, Maria shook her head slightly. Would Viorica understand? Would she realize it was better not to talk about Tata's disappearance when the little girls would hear?

Viorica did not ask again. She gazed back at her mother and, in that instant, was forced to grow up. The difficulty of her young life thrust her from innocent childhood into a brutal adult world.

The mother and three children huddled against the masonry stove that warmed their side of the house. Its comforting bulk was their only heat source, but it was adequate, even now during the late winter of 1956.

Maria could hear *Margareta* stoke the stove with coal. She shifted her daughters on her lap. What would she have done without the dear old couple from whom they were renting two rooms?

Maria did not know how she could have survived the ordeal when the secret police took *Cornel* away if it had not been for Margareta and *Ioan*. They had come over and comforted her and held her while she wept. Most important, they had prayed with her.

Now she sat, rocking her little girls in her lap, one arm around Viorica. Nights were the worst. Even putting the little girls into her own bed did not make up for the empty space in her heart. The space only Cornel could fill. Maria sighed deeply.

A thump outside the door of the entry shook the house.

Maria jerked her head quickly toward the sound. The drowsy girls stirred and whimpered.

Maria heard the outside door open. Then without warning, the door into the room crashed open. Four men, bundled in military coats and fur hats, burst into the room.

With a cry of alarm, Maria sprang up, clasping her daughters possessively to her breast.

"Get dressed! You are under arrest!" The head official spoke in a cold, hard voice.

"No! I cannot come with you! I must stay with my children!" Maria cried out in anguish.

"Your children must come too. We will put them in a secure place." The officer reached for Viorica's arm.

Wild-eyed in alarm, the girls clung to their mother. Feeling faint, Maria began to shiver uncontrollably.

"Get your coats! We must leave immediately!" The commanding voice filled the small room.

"No!" Maria screamed. Panic-stricken, strength coursed into her limbs again. "I cannot let you take my children away. I must stay with them!" Desperation filled her mother heart. She clung tightly to her children.

The other officers moved into action. They came forward and pried the girls from their mother's arms.

Lidia screamed in fear. Natalia and Viorica lunged desperately for their mother, their little fingers grasping her sleeves and skirt.

Maria fell to her knees. She began crying loudly. "Oh, Lord, look down upon Your child! Have mercy! Oh, Lord, have mercy on my children! Don't let this happen!" She turned to the officers who were wrapping coats around her little ones. "Oh, sirs! Have you no mercy? Have you no pity on a mother and her children? Think of your own little ones! Think of your wives! Oh, have mercy on us! Please, don't take my children from me!"

The door opened again, and Ioan and Margareta came into the crowded room.

"Oh, Maria!" Margareta's quavery voice was almost lost in the confusion. "What are they doing to you?"

Margareta tried to reach her young friend, but an officer held her back. "Who are you?" he barked with authority. "Get out!"

Maria struggled wildly to get free from another officer's grasp. "Margareta! Ioan! They are taking my children away!"

Her heartbreaking cry galvanized the old couple into action. Ioan, despite his age, moved swiftly to where an officer was trying to stuff Natalia's arms into her coat. "Natalia!" he croaked with emotion.

With a cry, Natalia freed herself and flung her arms around Ioan's legs.

"Sirs!" Ioan's voice rose above the clamor. "Leave the children with us! We will care for them!" With boldness he continued, "You will have big problems with the children if you take them away! They know us! We will care for them!"

The chief officer wavered. He glanced at the other men.

Somehow, Margareta had gotten Lidia into her arms. Viorica clung to the old lady, trembling in fear. Her brown eyes were enormous as she looked up at the officer.

"Oh, please!" Maria's broken voice pleaded, "take me, but leave my children! My darling girls!" She began to cry.

There was never a voiced concession. The chief official suddenly propelled Maria out the door, her coat hastily thrown around her shoulders.

She pressed her hands over her ears to drown out the wails of her children as she was forced rapidly along the snowy path, through the gate, and into a waiting car.

"For aiding and abetting your husband, Cornel *Florescu*, in spreading anti-government propaganda, we sentence you, Maria Florescu, to three months in prison." The wooden hammer struck the top of the judge's desk.

"Next!" he said wearily as Maria was led away between two guards.

Maria's breast heaved with emotion as she felt herself being propelled out of the courtroom. In a daze she entered the same black car that had brought her here the night before.

The drive from the courthouse to the prison was short. Maria sat perfectly still as they whisked through the snowy streets. Nothing looked familiar. Everything seemed unreal.

Her children! Oh! What had happened to her little girls? She turned frantically to the guard beside her. "Please, where are my children? Did they leave them with our neighbors? Did they take them away? Oh, please tell me! I must know!"

"Quiet!" the guard shouted after his first startled look at the young woman beside him. "I know nothing about your case. I know nothing about your children!"

Maria dissolved into a weeping huddle. She was hardly aware of being taken out of the car and thrust into a cell. Her heart was pounding wildly. All she could say, over and over, was, "Oh, Lord! Protect my children! Don't let them be taken away! Protect them!"

As she lay on her hard bunk that night, Maria could not sleep. Miraculously, she had a bed to herself. There was only one other woman in the cell with four bunks.

Her heart was shattered. She was scarcely aware of her barren surroundings, or even that she was not alone. The other woman also seemed lost in her own misery, and did not say anything to the weeping mother.

"Why, God? Oh, why did You allow this to happen? Was it not enough to have Cornel taken away? How is it possible that I, too, must be ripped away from my little girls, and endure prison for three months?" On and on Maria prayed, sometimes sobbing, sometimes weary and spent from her emotions.

The heavy, musty bedcover kept her body warm enough. She had not eaten since her arrest, but she was not hungry. She yearned only for one thing: her children.

In her semi-delirium, she heard voices. She stilled her every nerve. Was that Lidia's cry? She sprang out of bed and went to the barred door.

There was no sound. Silence that became louder and louder to her straining ears mocked her.

With a whimper, she returned to bed, there to lie in anguish.

For a minute, she visualized her daughters with Margareta and Ioan. She could picture the comforting old woman and her husband, gently rocking the weeping girls to sleep. The girls had often spent time with the old couple. They were like grandparents to them. Maria tried to tell herself that everything was well with her children.

Her thoughts turned to Cornel. It had been two days before her arrest that he had not come home from a late night visit with a sick man. Long into the night she had waited. Fear had clutched her heart, and she had prayed earnestly for her husband's safety.

Religious persecution was nothing new for Maria. Her father had been arrested for preaching the Gospel when Maria was only a child. She remembered the long years they had waited for him to return home. But he had never come home. One day they received notice that he had died of an accident in prison. They never found out where he was buried.

The authorities knew about the group of Christians in their village. The gathering of the believers was not a new thing. Everyone who repented of their sins and took on the name of Christian knew the cost of discipleship. For years, arrests, beatings, and prison terms had been the lot of the believers here in this Romanian village.

Yet, when Cornel's father brought news of Cornel's arrest, Maria was jolted. When Cornel had been ordained to the ministry, she thought she had prepared herself for his arrest. It was certain that the pastors of their church would face arrest and imprisonment. And when she had seen how willingly Cornel had accepted the call and had not allowed the government's threat to deter him from his calling, her own faith in God had been strengthened.

That's how it had been all through their marriage. When Maria had anguished over Natalia's sickly body after she had been born, it was Cornel who shored up her faith and gave her the needed encouragement to trust the baby's healing to the Lord. He was a tower of strength to her.

But now, Cornel was in prison and she was all alone. When she had realized she had to face life without her husband for as long as he was in prison, she had been devastated. She was plagued by the fear that he would be killed, like her father had been.

Her husband and children had ben taken from her, and she had no friends near by. In her anguish, she wordlessly turned to God.

When Maria had been fifteen, she had felt the need of repentance. Raised in a Christian home, she still knew that the faith her parents had was not enough to save her. The pastors taught clearly that every person must make his own decision, and it was only with a personal faith in the shed blood of Jesus that sins are forgiven. Maria felt the need for a Savior and repented.

Her joy in the Lord led her into a deep walk with God. Difficult as it was, she read her father's Bible and memorized large portions of the Word. Under her mother's diligent tutoring, Maria became firmly rooted in her faith.

Now, in spite of her anguish over her husband's absence and her little ones' welfare, Maria found comfort in her faith. She clung desperately to the memorized Word and forced her weary mind to repeat passages again and again.

———————

Days melted into each other. Maria, like countless prisoners before her, kept track of time. Marks scratched on the walls of her cell were proof that many a prisoner had tried to separate the monotony of days into individual blocks of time.

But one obsessive thought would not leave her. What was happening to her children? During the daytime, Maria could convince herself that they were all in God's hands and He was caring for them. She forced herself to believe that they were with Margareta and Ioan, being lovingly cared for.

But during the night, terror surged in. Black clouds of doubt engulfed her. Her frantic mind pictured her daughters being torn away from her neighbors' loving arms. She visualized them being thrust into a cold, bleak orphanage to be raised in a loveless environment where they were taught there is no God. They would forget her and Cornel. They would forget God!

Instead of spending their evenings by the side of their parents, listening to stories from the Bible, they would heartlessly be forced into beds with countless other children. Instead of carefully prepared food and individual care, they would have to feed at the common table and learn to fend for themselves. Maria groaned in anguish as her tormented mind harassed her with these horrible nightmares. Or were they nightmares? They could be true! She did not know!

"Please!" she said in a whisper when the guard brought the usual cup of tepid tea and a slice of dry bread one morning. "Please! Sir! Can you help me?"

The middle-aged guard was used to this. He completely ignored Maria's whisper. He clanged the tin mug on the shelf, slapped the bread beside it, and moved on.

Maria sat on her bunk, wrapping her fingers around the mug.

When the guard came back to collect the mugs, she tried a bolder approach. "I will pay you well if you bring me word about my children. I have money."

It was a daring plan. Usually, no money was mentioned when a bribe was offered. That was too risky. One only made allusions to money.

The guard stopped and stared at Maria. Looking deep into her worried face, he hesitated. Perhaps he saw what happens to the soul of a woman who has been robbed of her children. Perhaps he saw the care-lined face of a youthful woman grown old before her time. He hesitated.

A shout from the end of the corridor brought him to his senses. He buried the pity that had risen, grabbed the mugs from the shelf and sent them clanging into the container. He strode off furiously.

The next morning, Maria waited with anticipation for the tea and bread to arrive. She heard the guard come down the hall. With pounding heart, she clutched her small purse in her hand. Would it be enough?

When she had found her money purse in her coat pocket the first night of her arrest, Maria knew it was a miracle from the

Lord. After Cornel had been arrested, she had taken the little money they had hidden and put it in a cloth bag. She planned to give it to her widowed mother for safekeeping, but had failed to deliver it before her arrest. Now it was her only hope of news about her daughters.

The footsteps slowed, then stopped at her door. It was a different guard! Maria groaned in dismay. Her plan had failed.

As the hours passed, Maria began to realize that she never really had a good plan. It was more an act of desperation. Still, she thought she had to get word of her family, her children, but there was no way! All day long, she sat in despair.

"I will never leave thee, nor forsake thee." Over and over, Maria repeated this verse. She felt forsaken, yet her faith in God's Word was strong enough that she believed and clung to this promise.

God rewarded her. Gradually, her worry gave over to trust. It had to, she realized, or she would lose her mind. Already her mental state was deteriorating. She began to pray without ceasing.

And in loving response, the Spirit from above ministered to her. The One Who has promised to be a husband to the widows and a father to the fatherless comforted and strengthened the mother who longed for her children and her husband.

No words can ever tell and no books can ever be printed that can explain just how the compassionate and tender love of Jesus ministers to aching hearts. But He does. The Holy Spirit brought rest to the broken mother's heart who was weeping for her children.

It was not that Maria forgot her children, her little girls. No, a thousand times no! She did not forget her husband! She did not forget her own plight!

But in spite of it all, she found rest. Placing her aching heart, her weary mind, and her wrecked life into the hands of Jesus, Who said, "Come unto me, all ye that labor and are heavy-laden, and I will give you rest," Maria found rest.

The battle was fought not only once, but many times. Over and over Maria had to take all the broken pieces of her life and give them to her Savior before she found rest—sweet rest.

Maria almost ran, as she left the train station. She tried to force herself to slow down, for it was at least a thirty minute walk from the station to her house.

The three months were finally over. Maria was released and given enough money to buy a train ticket back to her hometown.

Three months is long enough for someone in prison to forget what it is like to be "outside." Many ex-prisoners are at first bewildered by the overwhelming change in their lives and savor every moment of the first day of their freedom.

But Maria had no time to think of how wonderful it was to be free. She hardly glanced around as she walked through the late April sunshine toward home. She was going home!

Was she really going home? What would she find there? More important, who would she find there? Her heart raced at the very thought.

Down the sidewalk the distraught mother bolted. Distraught? Yes, even though she had given the care of her little girls into the hands of the loving Father and had released the unknown by faith because she could not bear the burden alone, her heart expanded with maternal love and anxiety until she thought it might burst.

Once, she sank down on a backless bench beside the road to get her breath. Her inactivity in prison had weakened her. Or was it her heart's yearning toward her family? Was it not knowing whether she would see her children at home, or find an empty house? Maria panted at the very thought.

"Lord, how can I bear it? How can I go through this? What if my children are not there? What will I do?" Maria felt as though she could not think clearly. One part of her wanted to race home to see if her precious daughters were there. Another part of her was like lead, heavy and frozen, not wanting to know, lest she find nothing but an empty house, feel nothing but empty arms.

Once more, the Spirit brought calmness to her soul. Maria got up from the bench and hurried on.

Yes, hurried. She was willing to know the truth. If the children were not there, she would do all she could to find out where they were. She would go to the ends of the earth to find her little girls and clasp them once more in her aching arms. If Cornel was still in prison, she would go by herself. God would help her.

She could see the wooden fence around the house. She saw some of the neighbors. But she did not stop to ask if they knew whether her children were still with Margareta and Ioan. She just walked faster.

Her shaking hand lifted the latch. She swung the wooden gate open and entered.

"Viorica! Natalia! Oh, Lidia!" She called out with passion, with a hunger for love. The cry of her voice reflected the emotion, the longing of a mother for her children.

Even as her shoes scraped the stones on the path in the yard, she heard something from inside the house. Her heart leaped within her!

Children's voices! Oh, glory be to God! Children's voices!

She was at the door. Flinging open the last barrier between them, Maria swung it open.

There they were! All three of them!

"Oh, my darlings! Oh, my dear children!" Maria wept in joy as she knelt down on the wooden floor and opened her arms.

Margareta and Ioan were there, weeping tears of joy as they saw the mother and her children reunited. Ioan raised his hands toward heaven and praised the God of mercy for letting this part of the family be together again.

Lidia, bewildered by all the commotion, looked long and deeply into her mother's face and then turned to old Margareta. She whimpered and reached for the woman who had been her mother for the past three months.

Maria understood. She willingly passed her into the dear old lady's arms, and returned to her two oldest daughters.

Natalia stroked her mother's face over and over. Viorica hid her face against Maria, and cried broken-heartedly. No longer did she try to be brave for her sisters' sakes. No longer did she feel the weight of responsibility on her seven-year-old shoulders. Mama was home! Mama could take over now. She sobbed in relief.

With her arms wrapped around her two oldest daughters and Lidia safe in Margareta's familiar arms, Maria closed her eyes and began to pray. Not in words, just deep utterances from her spirit poured out in praise to God.

Several years passed before Cornel was released and the family was all back together again. For many years more, persecution continued to rage against the band of believers in southern Romania. But they persevered. They continued to trust in God for their salvation and for their help in time of trouble.

God never failed those who truly called out to Him in heartfelt supplication. Some, He delivered from the hands of the government and spared from prison and torture. Others, He allowed to suffer for the sake of the Kingdom. But every one who loved Him unto the end, He took home with Him where there were no more separations and no more tears. He Himself wiped all the tears from their eyes as He welcomed them home.

For Maria, her faith in the Lord was strengthened. Even today, tears come to her eyes when she talks of the time of separation from her little girls. But her faith in God is evident as she calmly tells of the rest she found when her mother heart was grieving beyond comprehension. She still praises God for the miracle of finding her girls at home, and is deeply humbled by the love of God that allowed her to clasp her small children in her arms again.

9

Spy at the Wedding

There are times when we think those who were persecuted under Communism bravely endured everything. However, they faced severe trials and temptations to "adapt." Yet the Lord was faithful in giving a boldness that comes from having a living relationship with Jesus Christ.

The man sitting in his apartment had no privacy to prepare his sermon. He was alone only in that the rest of his family was sleeping. His wife *Anya* lay on the cot that served as a sofa by day and their bed by night. Her regular, deep breathing told *Pioter* she was sleeping. *Lilya*, five years old and their youngest, had been sleeping for hours now. Their two teenage sons were sleeping in the entry on cots lining the wall and the girls, all five of them, were fast asleep in the second room.

Pioter did not have a study to seclude himself. There were no rows of books to express some commentator's thoughts for difficult passages of scripture, and no handy reference Bible. But he was used to this. He knew nothing else.

The Christian life had not been easy for Pioter. Ever since his conversion in 1936, when he was sixteen years old, he had experienced hardships. At least, they were hardships as man thinks, but God had turned those times of trial and persecution into times of growth and deep spiritual refreshing.

Yet, Pioter was human. There were definitely times when he

grew weary of the constant stress and the very real threat of being killed for his faith in Christ. He had many vivid reminders of the dangers that he faced daily.

Pioter shifted on the hard-back wooden chair. Bending over the table, he studied the written Word closely. Tomorrow he was to preach at the wedding of two Christian young people from their fellowship, and he wanted to be ready.

"Preach the Gospel of Jesus Christ!" The voice that whispered to him was distinct. Pioter recognized the leading of the Holy Spirit as he read the text.

"Will that mean another prison term? More harassment? More interrogations? Perhaps even prison for life this time?" Pioter glanced over at his sleeping wife. The light shone softly on her face, which was perfectly at rest.

Pioter's mind went back to one of the first trials he had experienced. He had been just a young man, drafted to serve in the Soviet army and filled with a desire to be a witness for his Lord and Savior, Jesus Christ.

Well, the opportunity had come quickly. His conscience had not allowed him to take the oath of allegiance to an earthly kingdom, and that had marked him for discrimination. However, he had been forced to go along with his unit and face the German army. As soon as he could, he had gathered all the soldiers around him and led them in prayer. He had asked the Lord to be merciful to them and begged God to forgive mankind for the terrors of warfare.

With bombs landing all around them, Pioter had continued praying for their protection. When the skirmish was over, Pioter and the rest of the survivors were sent back to the barracks. There, Pioter had been brought before his captain and sentenced to death for preaching to the boys.

The *Kalashnikov* had been pointed at Pioter's head, and he had fully expected to be killed, but the gun was not fired. The gun was then pointed straight at his chest. Again, Pioter thought he would be killed.

For some reason, the trigger was never pulled. Instead, Pioter was forced to do hard manual labor in the army. He had not been allowed to mingle freely with the soldiers.

Pioter ran his hand through his hair. The memories that flooded his mind were opening a door to another incident. The clock ticked steadily beside him, on into the night.

After he was married, Pioter had started to work with youths. Not just the youths of the church, but any he could contact. The success of his work did not go unnoticed by the authorities. This was after the Socialist government had legislated mandatory registration of all churches and had outlawed any independent groups from meeting. But Pioter had continued his work, and one day, after what he had thought was a secret baptism for a score of young people, he had been arrested.

At first he had been incarcerated with several other pastors, but later was separated from the believers and pushed into a cell filled with hardened criminals.

There, he had feared for his life. But again, God was with him and he had been able to win the favor of his cell mates after he began sharing the Good News of Jesus Christ.

Now, here in his apartment, Pioter faced another challenge. Was he willing to listen to the Spirit and preach the Gospel at the wedding tomorrow? For some reason, in the dark of the night, doubts wanted to overtake him, and he wrestled with his conscience.

He knew that the net was tightening around him once more. He was very aware of being shadowed constantly as he went from his home to meet with the brethren. During the past twenty years he had been watched, arrested at times, and fined for his work. Now, he sensed his life was in danger again.

"You can preach a message to the young couple getting married," a voice from somewhere suggested. "No one really expects you to preach anything that could get you in trouble. Think of your family. They have gone through enough already. Tell the people how a good marriage is important. Surely you have already done your duty of preaching the Gospel."

Yes, Pioter was human. He grappled with very real issues. His life was already hard; the years of toil and trouble showed on his forty-year-old face.

Pioter buried his face in his hands. His spirit groaned within him. Outside, the warm April night wrapped dark arms around the windows.

The setting was as beautiful as anyone could wish for a wedding. All the apple trees in the village were blooming and early flowers brightened the borders of the yards. The house where the wedding was to be held was freshly whitewashed.

The guests were assembling in the yard. Some were already sitting on benches, on chairs brought out from the houses, or on improvised seating formed from planks. An aisle down the center led to a sunny spot where a podium was waiting.

Many guests had been invited. As the time drew closer for the service to begin, more and more people came through the yard gate and stood in clusters in the back. More than three hundred people were gathered, waiting for the service to begin.

A hymn wafted upward through the blossoming fruit trees. Men and women's voices rose in beautiful harmony. The strains drifted into the house where the wedding party was making final preparations.

The bridal couple, *Igor* and Claudia, had already been to the office in the city where the civil wedding had taken place. With their parents and only a few witnesses, they had exchanged their vows and signed the documents, declaring them man and wife. But since they were both Christians, they still did not really feel married until they had exchanged their vows before their Christian fellowship, and received their blessing.

Pioter was sitting among the guests. The pastors in the underground churches did not conspicuously gather together in groups. That would make it too easy for any informers to spot the leaders and try to surround them.

Maybe we will be left alone during this wedding, Pioter couldn't help thinking. Weddings in their country were largely unhindered by the government, but recently persecution against the believers had been stepped up. Pioter wondered if any gathering would be safe. Were informers planted among the group of guests gathered here today? Pioter glanced around him. It would be easy to hide in a group this size. Pioter gave a sigh. Anya, sitting beside him, glanced at him. She placed her hand on his.

Pioter smiled at his wife. She could sense that he was worried.

He knew she was praying for him. Praying that he would have courage to do the right thing. Courage to speak whatever the Spirit laid upon his heart to preach.

The first message was over. As the choir softly sang, the bridal pair came out of the house and slowly walked toward the podium. The attendants trailed along behind them.

Ahh! So perfect was the setting, so beautiful the bride, so handsome the groom! Bouquets of tulips and apple blossoms graced the space around the podium. Birds twittered among the arching branches of the blooming trees and the sun shone gently over their entire world.

Yet, when Pioter got up to begin his sermon, his heart was beating rapidly. For some reason, he felt fear clutching at his heart, stifling his breath, and stammering his speech.

Then, facing the crowd of expectant faces, he drew a deep breath. Igor and Claudia were right in front of him, lifting their joyful faces toward him. A hush spread over the congregation.

"Dearly beloved!" Pioter's voice suddenly rang out loud and clear in the silent air. "We are gathered here to celebrate the wedding of our brother and sister, Igor and Claudia! But not just to celebrate their marriage! We are gathered together this morning to worship our Lord and Savior, Jesus Christ, the Son of the living God!"

Throughout the audience heads nodded in agreement.

Pioter continued, "Since we have gathered to worship the Lord Jesus Christ, let us stand and pray to Him!" He led in prayer, asking the presence of the Lord to be with them and asking a special blessing on the bride and groom.

Then, he opened his Bible. "I will read a beautiful story this morning of a wonderful happening. A story explaining what we must do to be saved from our sins and from the wrath to come!" Turning to the Gospel of John, chapter 3, he began to read the stirring account of Jesus talking with Nicodemus.

It was a full-fledged salvation message. Such was his burden for the unsaved, so strong his desire to present the Gospel to the many who had never heard the Good News, that not once did Pioter look at his notes. He just preached from his heart, filled with the Spirit.

For an hour he preached. His eyes searched the crowd, pleading with them to consider the end of the wicked. He spoke of the glorious release of the sinner from his burden of sin, the unmatched joy and peace that enter into the hearts of those who believe and repent, and the cost of following Jesus.

An average-sized, middle-aged man in a gray suit sat at the edge of the crowd, toward the back. His quick, darting eyes took in everything. At times, he made notes in a small tablet that he secreted inside his jacket. But most of the time, he listened intently, watching everything.

Even though the man was sitting in the shade under an apple tree, Pioter noticed him. In spite of the huge crowd, there was something about him that arrested his attention. It was as though Pioter were two people. One part of him was speaking passionately to the crowd, the other part watching and noticing the man in the gray suit.

Nevertheless, Pioter preached. As the hour wore on, he began the invitation. " 'Come unto me, all ye that are heavy laden . . . and learn of me . . . for my yoke is easy and my burden is light!' These are the words of Jesus Himself. He gave His life for us so that we can know what living is. All the persecutions anyone has to bear for the Name of Christ are as nothing compared to the joy and peace He gives to all those who respond to His love. Our future with Jesus in heaven is no comparison to those who die in their sins and are cast away from Him into hell.

"Many of our brethren and sisters are today suffering for their faith. They suffer from overexposure to the rain and snow. They suffer in solitary confinement. They are separated from their families. They are beaten and tortured for their faith.

"Yet they stand. Why? Because they do not love their lives, but they love their Lord, Jesus Christ. They are willing to suffer all these things, for they are looking for another kingdom that is not of this world. This kingdom is in heaven!"

The man in the gray suit stared at Pioter. He seemed amazed at Pioter's boldness. There was almost a look of bewilderment on his face.

Undeterred, Pioter gave the call for repentance. He earnestly pled with the people to consider their ways.

More than twenty young people responded. Weeping and crying out to God, they knelt on the grass beside the podium. Brethren and sisters from the group knelt beside the repentant ones, praying with them. Truly, the Spirit of God was there.

Songs of rejoicing spread throughout the crowd of worshiping people. The hearts of young men and women were being changed! Souls were being saved! A greater rejoicing than just a wedding could bring was in the air! People were being born again!

Truly, it was a beautiful place. As Igor and Claudia faced each other, pledging their lives together as one in the Name of Jesus, the air was vibrant with the joy of newborn souls. Yet, unplanned as it was, there was an orderliness, a calmness that settled over the entire meeting.

"Sir, do you believe in God?" Pioter's question was direct and took the gray-suited man by surprise.

"Ah, no I don't!" The reply was quick and forced.

The two men stood facing each other. As soon as the service had ended, while the tables were being prepared for the wedding feast, Pioter had sought out the man he had noticed during the service.

"Then, friend, in all due respect, you are to be pitied." Pioter said the words sincerely and earnestly.

The man in gray shifted his eyes. Then he said in perfect frankness. "How can you persuade such a large group of people to follow what we educated people know is merely a myth? You spoke of a mythical person and you speak of a mythical place." Then, almost as if to himself, he added, "Even the young people, educated as they are, believe you!"

Pioter's reply was quick. "That's because we know it is not a myth. We are not questioning whether what we believe is true or not. We know it is true! We know it because it works for us! We experience the presence of our God from day to day! It is not difficult to persuade people when they recognize the truth!"

The man was silent for a moment. "But you are going against the government! You are breaking the law! You have not registered your church, therefore your meetings are illegal," the man said sternly, staring directly into Pioter's eyes.

"We must preach the truth!" Pioter said respectfully. "As you heard, our faith is not just a faith to live for, it is a faith to die for. We must obey God rather than man. Man has no right to dictate what we believe. Even our constitution declares that we have the right to worship as we believe."

"I feel sorry for you!" The eyes of the man grew cold and hard. "You will not win. We will yet see all of you ignorant people destroyed and our land freed from such weaklings as you." He brushed past Pioter and left.

In the days that followed, Pioter found himself waiting for something. He tried to go about his duties with faith and confidence, yet a cloud hung over him.

He felt sure the man in the gray suit was an informer. The information he had gathered during the wedding service could be used against any of the speakers at the wedding. And Pioter knew that he himself was a prime target. He could be charged for speaking without permission from the authorities. He could be charged for corrupting the minds of the youth. For that alone, he could be sentenced to years in prison. The communists were determined that no youths should believe in God and join any Christian organization. He would be watched closely, for they would expect a baptism to follow after so many youths had repented and confessed Jesus as their Lord. Yes, Pioter felt that dark shadow.

Daily he prayed. He tried to prepare himself for whatever lay ahead. He shared his feelings with his wife, and often they prayed together.

Less than two weeks after the wedding, Pioter was sitting in his apartment, resting after work. He picked up the local newspaper and idly glanced at the headlines. There was not much of interest to him. He turned the pages.

Suddenly he gave an exclamation. "Anya!" he called.

"Yes, Pioter! What is it?" She hurried to her husband's side.

"Look! It is that man! He died!"

Together, they looked at the black and white photograph. It was the man in the gray suit! In the picture, he even wore the same gray suit that he had worn at the wedding. Now he was dead!

". . . died of complications due to infection following a very brief illness." Anya read the words aloud in a wondering tone.

She looked at Pioter. "Do you think the threat is gone now that he has died?" It was a question neither of them could answer.

Pioter looked at the paper again, at the man in gray who had been his enemy. "Oh, Anya! Think of his soul! He said he was an atheist! Oh, Lord, have mercy on him!"

———————————————

The heavy cloud that had hung over Pioter seemed to lift somewhat, as though the immediate peril he felt had disappeared with the death of the informer. Still, as always, a sense of danger remained his constant, tireless companion.

But in the following days, a sense of awe filled Pioter. The presence of God was very real to him. Over and over again Pioter was reminded of the Bible verse, "God is not mocked."

As the church continued to grow and the number of believers increased, Pioter often remembered the words of the man who was now dead: "We will yet see all of you ignorant people destroyed."

Jesus had promised that His church would prevail. However fierce the enemy raged, the church of Jesus Christ would never be destroyed. It would continue in spite of persecution.

10

Lidia's Passion for Christ

Great things are done by people who love their Lord, like "Lidia" of this story. I have met "Lidia" and the faith she embraced so long ago is still a driving force in her life. She has since gone home to be with the Lord. This story happened in Ukraine during World War II.

Lidia knew she must do it. A part of her quailed inside, thinking of the repercussions that were sure to follow. Yet there was no alternative. She had to be true to the leading of her Lord.

"*Yevgeny,* dear. There is something I must tell you." Lidia began bravely. They were sitting in their room, getting ready for bed. Their firstborn son lay securely in his mother's arms, sleeping.

Her husband looked at her sharply. His eyes burned with expectancy. "Well," was his quick answer.

"I-I want to be baptized. I must be baptized!" There—it was out. Each word fell heavily between the couple, simple, yet weighty.

"No!" His answer was swift, expected. "I forbid it! You shall not be baptized by anyone else. You were already baptized by the priest when you were born. That is enough!" Yevgeny's eyes blazed as he glared at his young wife. "Why did you ever listen to your *dyadya's* message? I wish we had never seen him since he returned from the army! The heretical teachings he brought home with him have brought nothing but ruin to us!"

Lidia's heart lurched with pain as her husband began his tirade.

She gently rocked her tiny son on her lap.

"None of our family has fallen for this new—this heresy! I cannot imagine what my parents would say if you would be baptized. But you will not do it, I say! I simply will not allow you to be baptized! That is all there is to it!"

"But I must!" Lidia burst out in anguish. "Yevgeny, dear! I have to make a confession of what Jesus has done for me! He died for me so that my sins can be forgiven! He shed His lifeblood for my sins! The least I can do is be obedient to His will, and seal my faith with water baptism." The words came out in a rush. Lidia looked pleadingly at her husband. "You come, too!"

She caught her breath. For Yevgeny had risen and stood menacingly over her.

"You will stay right here in this house! I will see to it that you are not baptized!" Then he turned and stormed out of the bedroom.

"Oh, God! I come to You in this hour of need!" Instinctively, Lidia began praying. She sat rocking her son, and pouring out prayers that had no words, only deep, intense feelings.

This was not the first time she had brought up her desire to be baptized. After she had repented, she immediately desired baptism. Her whole heart was caught up in her desire to live for Christ and to speak of her faith. As soon as the ministers of her church planned to baptize the new believers, Lidia wanted to receive baptism.

Always Yevgeny's answer had been the same: No. To make matters worse, they lived with Yevgeny's parents who were as vehement against Lidia's faith in Jesus as Yevgeny was. Abuse and scorn were heaped on her defenseless head, day after day.

Yet, a burning desire drove the young mother on. In her prayers, she yearned after God and, over and over, told Him her heart's desire. "I know that You accept me as Your child, but I want to make this declaration before Your children that I am Your child! Please, Lord, let me seal my faith with water baptism!"

"Hush, dear child! Hush! Hush!" Lidia walked the floor of their room. Tears were streaming down her face and dripping onto her swaddled infant. There was no light in the dark room, yet she knew it so well she could walk from one end to the other. Her baby kept screaming until Lidia finally got herself together enough to realize that she must feed her son in order to quiet him.

This was the night that the baptism was to be held. That was why she was a prisoner in her own bedroom. Lidia could hardly believe it.

All evening, she had felt watched. After Yevgeny and his father came home from work, they had all settled down around the table in an uneasy silence. Silently, they had eaten their potatoes and bread.

Lidia had been tense, wondering just what would happen when she prepared to leave. For she had been determined to face the consequences and be baptized. Just how she would do it, she had not been sure.

After supper, she had taken little *Misha* into her bedroom to nurse him. That was when it had happened.

Scarcely had she settled herself on the side of the bed when someone shut the door. Then, she heard a sound she had never heard before from the inside of their bedroom. It was the sound of a key being turned in the door and the click of the lock as it firm-ly slid into place.

In alarm and consternation, Lidia had jumped up and tried the door. It was locked! She had pounded on the door, calling out, "Yevgeny! Let me out!"

Misha had burst into a wail, screaming at the top of his little lungs. In her distraction, Lidia had not immediately taken care of his needs, but continued pounding on the door.

She could hear nothing outside of the door. Her baby's cries drowned out any voice or noise from the living room.

"Hush! Hush!" Lidia picked up her baby and tried to settle her-self on the bed again. She tried to comfort her infant son, yet, she was actually speaking to her own heart, trying to regain her own composure.

Finally, Misha stopped his crying. He snuggled close to his mother, feeling comfort wash over him in warm waves as he nursed.

Lidia stared straight ahead. How could they do this to her? How could Yevgeny allow her to be locked in their own room! A dry sob caught in her throat.

Misha began to cry again. Little as he was, he could sense that something upsetting was happening. Something was wrong!

Lidia forced herself to be calm and regain control. She could not become distraught and bring discomfort to her son! Turning to the Lord, she began pouring out her heart to Him.

"Dear Jesus! I come to You! You see where I am. Locked up in my own room. You know how I want to be baptized tonight. Now, I see it is impossible. Yet, in my heart, You know how much I love You! Take that love as a gift from my heart. I surrender myself to You!"

Could she? Yes, she could. Lidia laid her now—sleeping son carefully on top of the clothes wardrobe. Guarding Misha with one arm, she drew herself up from the bed, wriggling on her stomach until she could scramble onto the top of the wardrobe. She listened intently to see if her movements had been heard by anyone in the other room. There was no sound.

Crouched on the wardrobe, she pushed against the square trapdoor above her. Slowly, carefully, she pushed the wooden boards away. Stale air from the attic washed down over her.

An inner strength made it possible to take the still sleeping infant and put him on the floor of the attic in the dark. Drawing herself up through the opening, she crept cautiously across the wooden boards of the attic and went out the door at the gable end of the house. With sure steps, Lidia climbed down the ladder that always leaned against the house, for they used the attic as an additional storage area.

Through the night, the young mother sped, clutching her baby against her breast.

Yevgeny was in a towering rage. He opened the wardrobe door and grabbed Lidia's dresses. "I am not going to tolerate this! You went directly against my wishes! How did you dare endanger our baby's life and escape through the attic? You could have dropped him and injured him for the rest of his life!"

In his fury he threw an armload of dresses on the floor. He stomped on them and continued his tirade against his wife.

Lidia huddled on the bed, fear and dismay engulfing her. She had never seen Yevgeny this angry! Would he hit her?

Grabbing her hairbrush off the nightstand, he threw it against the wall. The brush ricocheted across the floor. Misha stirred in Lidia's arms. She brushed her still damp hair away from her face.

"When we found out you had escaped, we were extremely hurt that you had disobeyed us! This is a horrible disgrace for our family." Yevgeny could scarcely control himself. "You! A heretic! What is wrong with the village church?" He paced from one end of their room to the other.

"What a wife! I never dreamed when I married you that I was marrying someone who would deliberately go against my wishes! I knew you were different from the other village girls, that you had more spunk than they, but I never dreamed you would run away!" He shook his head in disbelief. His anger was abating rapidly. As he looked at Lidia, sitting on the bed, nursing Misha, he could not help but admire her grit. She had escaped with their infant through the trapdoor in the ceiling!

"How did you ever manage?" He gave a short burst of laughter. "Whatever gave you the idea that you could take Misha and go through the attic?"

Lidia looked pleadingly at her husband. "Yevgeny, don't you understand? I do want to obey you and be a submissive wife, but my Lord has greater claims on my life. I had to be baptized! Something in here," Lidia lifted her hand and placed it against her chest, "made me do it! If it was possible, I was going to go!"

"Well, it was not possible, but you still did it!" Then he laughed ruefully. "You are the only one who can do impossible things."

Lidia bent forward, resting her forehead on her right hand that gripped the plow. The cow had stopped, her gaunt sides heaving in the hot summer sun. Lidia's sweaty brow wet her hand. She was so exhausted. Her legs quivered with tiredness. As the sun beat down on her in the middle of the field, time seemed to stand still.

All morning, Lidia had been plowing the field with her cow. The overseer of the collective farm had made it clear that she was to have her plot finished by sundown. Even the times she had spent nursing the new baby had been short, for she feared the wrath of the overseer.

"Hup!" Lidia flicked the thin stick against the back end of her milk cow. With labored steps, the cow moved forward, pulling the plow.

It was more than two months ago that Yevgeny had been drafted into the army. Misha was now almost two years old, and the baby, little *Nadia*, was barely six months old. When the orders had come for Lidia to report to work on the collective farm, at first she had thought it impossible. She was a mother with two children! Her husband had been drafted into the army! How could she work?

But go she must. Orders were orders. Take the cow and go to work. Figure out how to manage the children. Leave them with your mother-in-law or put them into an orphanage. The overseer didn't care what happened to the children. They would be raised somehow.

Lidia cared! "I will die of starvation and allow my children to die before I will place them in an orphanage," she had told her mother-in-law. "I will not let someone raise my children who is not a Christian!"

Yevgeny's parents knew that their daughter-in-law meant what she said. They had seen the difference in Lidia's life after she had been baptized. No longer did they mock her for her faith, for the Lord had truly done a miracle in Lidia's life. Always cheerful and uncomplaining, she was sweeter than ever. Yevgeny grew to love his wife in a deeper way, even though he had never yielded to his wife's pleas to repent from his sins. Lidia had spent many hours praying for her husband and witnessing to him. But the strongest testimony had been her life.

Now, Misha stayed with his grandmother, and Lidia took the baby with her to the fields. Day after day, Lidia toiled with her cow, plowing the fertile Ukrainian soil.

When she reached the edge of the field, the cow refused to move. "You poor thing," Lidia sympathized. "You never were meant to be both a milk cow and a work animal." Indeed, the cow was almost no longer a milk cow. The daily hard work had almost dried her up. Barely a cup of milk could Lidia coax out of the twice daily milking.

A wail from little Nadia reached across the plowed field. "Stay here and rest, poor thing," Lidia told the cow. She walked across the rough soil toward her crying baby.

"Now, now, dear one," Lidia picked up her squalling daughter. "Mama is here." She settled her tired back against the tree trunk that provided shade for them both.

"I don't know, Lord, how much longer I will be able to work either. The cow is worn out and hardly gives milk anymore, and I feel as worn out as the cow. My daughter is not gaining weight as she should, and if the cow stops giving milk, we have nothing extra for Nadia. Let me know what You want me to do." Lidia prayed audibly, talking to God as though He were right beside her. He was right there, Lidia knew. Without Him, she would despair.

"I'm going to die," the man on the hospital cot moaned in agony. He tossed his head back and forth on the thin pillow. "I know—I'm going to die. I don't know—what will happen—to me! Please!" His eyes wide with fear, he pled with whoever would listen. "Help me! I don't want—to die!"

Lidia wrung out the white cloth in a bowl of clean water. She folded it, then began bathing the wounded soldier's forehead. His skin was hot and feverish.

"*Vitaly*," she said, looking at his chart. "Would you like to have me tell you of Someone who can prepare you for death? Someone who can give you eternal life in heaven?"

"Uh–h–h!" Vitaly grimaced. "Not—the priest. He—can't help. He's too busy—with other things."

"I'm not talking about the priest, sir. I'm talking about Jesus Christ, the Son of God. He is the only One who can save you. He can prepare you for death!"

Vitaly quit moving his head. He looked up at Lidia. "You're the one—who comes every day—to help me, aren't you? Ever since—I'm here, no one—really cared—except you. I'm just—another—

wounded soldier. But every day, you bathe my forehead—bring me—cold water. Who are you?"

Lidia smiled and wrung out the washcloth again. "I'm the cleaning lady," she said. She placed the cooling cloth on Vitaly's hot brow. "I scrub the floors, take the laundry downstairs and clean the rooms."

"You don't—have to help us—dying—wretches? You—do this on—your own?"

"Never mind. I want to. If I can do something for someone, something to help, I am glad to do it."

"You know—I'm going to die." Vitaly gasped as pain wrenched his body. "I'm getting—worse—every day. Just forget about me—like the rest," Vitaly gritted bitterly. "No more—use—helping me."

"It's like I have been telling you, sir. There is Someone who can help you! Someone who can prepare you for dying! Would you like to know about Him?"

Vitaly clenched his teeth against the pain. "Not—a priest. I can't stand them. They are just—like the rest of us. I lived—neighbor—to one in my city."

"No, no!" Lidia protested. "I will tell you of Jesus Christ. He can save your soul even now and deliver you from all your sins. I tell you, no one else can prepare you for the next life!"

"I wish—I could believe that!" Vitaly moaned again. "I have been a captain—in the army—stared at death—over and over. I was not afraid. But—now it's me—lying here—slowly dying." Fear filled his eyes again. "I am scared to die!" He closed his eyes and groaned, both in pain and in anguish of soul.

Lidia felt tears sting her own eyelids. Then, with a calm, sure voice she began. "Listen, sir. Jesus cares for everyone. He came to earth to teach us how to live. He was crucified for our sins. It was our sins that put Him on the cross. But He rose again from the dead! That is why we can go to heaven with Him after we die, if we repent from our sins and believe on Him!" Lidia spoke with passion.

"Tell me more." Vitaly spoke through a haze of pain. "I see—you believe in—what you say. Tell me—what to do! Oh! I would—do anything—to have the—assurance—I hear in your voice."

Beside the dying man's bed, Lidia ministered to Vitaly's soul. She told him about the condemnation that is on every person's life, about the sin that bars everyone from heaven. With gladness and joy, she told him about the blood of Jesus, shed for the forgiveness of sin. Any sin. Eagerly she told him about the new life that the repentant believer can have in Christ.

Vitaly listened. His yearning heart groped to understand. Finally, he whispered. "I want to repent. I want—to receive Jesus—my Savior."

Lidia bowed her head as he prayed. She wept with joy as she heard the dying soldier cry out to Jesus for forgiveness for his sins. Her voice mingled in praise with Vitaly's as she heard him thank Jesus for saving his soul.

"Thank you so much!" Vitaly breathed, spent. "What—is your name?"

"My name is Lidia. Brother, God bless you richly. Trust in Jesus for everything and He will be with you. He will never leave you nor forsake you."

"I believe that. I already have—peace and rest—that I never knew—possible. Even in all—my pain, I feel different. I think—I now have faith—that I am ready to die. Ready—to go to see Jesus—in heaven. Oh! It is not dying! It is the beginning—of eternal life! Thank You, Jesus!"

Lidia quietly left him, his eyes closed, lips moving in prayer.

With her own heart rejoicing, Lidia moved on to the next task. Whether it was mopping floors, cleaning up messes or simply bringing some suffering soul a cup of water, she did it all for the Lord.

Her days at the collective farm had ended. The cow had finally become so emaciated that Lidia took her to the market and sold her for what little she could get. Then, she had taken her two little children and moved into a room in a boarding house. Willing to do any work to feed her little family, she had hired herself out as a janitor in the hospital. The pay was extremely poor, but she earned enough to feed themselves. Now she lived close enough to her parents that she could leave the children with her aged mother. Both her father and her mother had become Christians, so Lidia felt at rest to leave the children with them while she went to work. Work she must, for wartime living was extremely difficult for everyone.

At the hospital, she found open doors to tell others about her Savior. At every opportunity, Lidia shared the Gospel. Many a sick and dying soldier, beyond hope in this world, eagerly listened to the glorious and saving story of Jesus Christ.

As often as she could, Lidia asked for news about Yevgeny. She had not heard from him since he had left for the front. Daily, she prayed for her husband's safety. But even more, she prayed for his salvation. Often, long into the night, the young woman interceded for the soul of the man she loved. Hard as it was, she finally rested her worrying heart into the arms of Jesus. Then, and only then, could she go to sleep and get her rest.

The hospital in *Kiev* was much larger than the village hospital she had just left, but Lidia thanked God over and over for leading her into the city. The work was not nearly as strenuous and, even better, she was able to spend more time with her children. During her lunch break, she could go home and be the mother she longed to be to her children. Both Misha and Nadia were now growing rapidly, as healthy as children should be.

Lidia continued her evangelistic efforts. The hospital was filled to capacity with soldiers, either recuperating or dying from war wounds. Her coworkers scoffed at her for "wasting her time" as they put it. But Lidia persevered. Her passion for Christ did not diminish.

Her passion to find news about Yevgeny did not diminish. She continued questioning everyone she could think of about news from her husband. She longed to hear from him.

Would the day ever come when she could stay at home with her children and be a homemaker once more? When would this terrible war end? The suffering and pain that resulted from the conflict filled the lives of all the people, and especially the hospital workers.

Then the terrible blow came. "Your husband is dead. Killed in action." The officer who informed Lidia of Yevgeny's death was used to bringing bad news. Yet it was always difficult to tell a wife that her hopes were gone.

"Tell me, please, sir!" Lidia breathed shakily. "How did he die? Did he say anything? What were his last words?"

The officer shook his head. "Sorry, madam. There is no information about that. The report just says that he was killed in action. That is all." He looked in pity at the slight young woman scarcely in her twenties. Hard work had not worn Lidia out. Rather, it had given her a strength of character that was evident to everyone she met. Or maybe it was her spirit that caused her face to glow . . . her faith in Christ.

"Oh, if I only could talk to someone who was there! I want so badly to know if he died a Christian!"

The officer shook his head. "I'm so sorry. That unit was never heard from again. I don't think there are any survivors."

Lidia reeled from the shock. That evening, as she knelt beside her sleeping children, she wept long and hard. Unanswered questions filled her mind. Did Yevgeny have time to repent before he breathed his last breath? Had he lain on some battle—torn soil, begging to God for forgiveness for his sins? Had his heart found rest in Jesus as His Savior?

"God, I will never know the answers. I know that Yevgeny knew the way to You. I will surrender all my unknown questions to You. That is the only way I can find rest for my broken heart."

The deep breathing of her children brought sharp reality to her plight. In the Soviet Union, it was difficult enough for a husband to raise a family. Now, Lidia would have to struggle to provide for her little children by herself. But even in that, Lidia found rest. Had God not promised He would be a husband to the widows who trusted in Him? She would trust.

Anton lay still in his hospital room. His head was heavily bandaged from the wound he had received in the war. At first, he had not known where he was. His last memory had been of a loud explosion, right beside his head, and then he had lost consciousness.

Now all he could do was lie here . . . and rest. Many times he had longed for rest when, day after day, they were forced into a ruthless advance against the Germans. They had been driving them out of Ukraine, back into occupied Poland. Then came the explosion.

He heard the rustle of a uniform next to his bed. A kind voice asked him if he wanted a drink. All he had to do was lick his lips, and a glass of water was tipped carefully against his mouth.

"Thank you," he whispered. Since he could not turn his head without pain shooting through his entire body, he tried to turn his eyes as far as he could. He could just make out the form of a slight woman, bending over the cot beside him. "Would you like a drink?" Anton heard her ask.

That was not the last time she ministered to him. Day after day, week after week, month after month, as Anton slowly fought to recover, this same woman brought a drink for him or attended to some other need he had. Not only for him, but also for the others.

Lidia, her name was, as he overheard her tell another soldier.

Then one day, the doctor diagnosed Anton with tuberculosis. Thus began his second battle. This dreaded disease hindered him from regaining back his strength. Although his head wound was slowly healing, he was still too weak to walk.

But at last, his strength began to return as the tuberculosis was beaten. His youthful body responded to the treatment, and Anton knew that soon he could leave the hospital. He would not have to go back to war, as he was far too weak to aid any army, but soon he would be strong enough to be released from the hospital.

"Lidia," Anton heard *Sasha*, one of the recuperating soldiers, ask one day, "what makes you different? Why have you always cared for us and brought us water whenever we needed it. I know you are not a nurse for I have seen you mopping the floor. Why do you do it?"

Lidia smiled as she was quick to do. "Because I want to help anyone I can. That is why. When Jesus was here on earth, He always helped those who needed help. Since I love Him, I want to do the same. Jesus puts that love in my heart for all people."

Anton knew that was true. Lidia never singled out just one person. Her care and concern was for everyone. And she did not do it because they were men. She never responded to any teasing.

Whenever a soldier tried to flirt with her, she told him firmly that he would have to stop it or she would not attend to him again. She was no pushover, that was plain.

Neither was this the first time that Anton had heard Lidia talk about Jesus. Sometimes she spent quite a long time talking about Jesus Christ to soldiers who cursed and swore in pain. Christ—the one who could deliver them from such language.

The day Anton was to be released, he waited until Lidia came on duty. Eagerly, he watched her as she came close to his bed.

"Lidia, I am going to be released today! I will be staying with my brother here in Kiev until I am stronger!"

"That is good!" Lidia shared his joy. "You need to thank God that He has healed you from your disease!" She reached for the waste can beside Anton's bed. "I want to invite you to come to church on Sunday. We always welcome visitors, and you can join the other soldiers who have been attending our worship services."

"Where is it?" Anton asked. Yes, he would go. He wanted to know more about what made Lidia different. What did she have that other people didn't have?

"You, too, can find forgiveness for your sins! Your heart can be washed clean and white by repenting from your sins and believing in the Lord Jesus Christ. Will you come and repent before the Lord? Will you identify with the people of God?"

Anton sat with the small group of soldiers who had been attending services in the home of Lidia's father. He looked over to where Lidia sat between her children. He had never seen her husband. Perhaps he was away at the war.

For over a month, he had been coming to listen. Something kept drawing him back to hear more of what the minister had to say.

For he saw that here were more people who had what Lidia had. The same fervency for the things of God, the same kindness toward everyone, the same compassion. That was what touched Anton's heart.

"Come, kneel down and ask the Lord to forgive your sins. Repent, and be saved!"

With rapidly beating heart, Anton responded. He wanted to

have what these people had. He wanted to find rest for his soul. Rising to his feet, he walked carefully, but steadily, toward the front.

The small group of believers began to sing softly as Anton knelt and, weeping, began to pray. He was willing to forsake all of his sins, and to follow the way of the Lord. He wanted Jesus to cleanse him and make him whiter than snow.

The minister knelt beside the young man and earnestly prayed for him. Joyful hearts rang out in praise that one more soul was being added to the kingdom.

"Here it is, Lidia. Here is the document from my village stating that I have never been married." Anton held out the official paper toward Lidia.

"Oh, Anton! I believed you! I . . . I just said that because I really don't know your history!" Lidia sighed and reached out for the paper. "But, Anton! How can I accept your proposal? What will people say if I marry someone nine years younger than I? Everyone will think I am taking advantage of you! Plus, I have Misha and Nadia! Anton, I don't see how it can work out!" A crease ran across Lidia's forehead as she talked.

They were standing outside the entrance to the apartment building where Lidia lived with her children. Anton well knew the time that Lidia got off from work, so he had met her here.

"Lidia, I have prayed about it, and I do feel the Lord leading me to ask you to marry me. I have talked with the minister about it and he heartily approves of our match. Do you not trust me?" Anton pleaded gently.

Lidia looked down at her shoes. Then, she lifted her eyes to Anton's face. "I do trust you, Anton. I . . . I just want to be sure. I don't want to make any mistakes. Both for me, and for my children. Will you give me more time, Anton? I don't want to hurt you in any way, but I must pray more about it. Is that all right?" She smiled up at him.

"Yes, Lidia. I will give you more time. I realize I have been thinking and praying about it much longer than you have. So, yes, I will be willing to wait."

Then he chuckled. "Do you want to keep the paper?"

Lidia laughed sheepishly. "No! When I asked how I could know whether or not you had ever been married, I never expected you to travel all the way to your village and get this document! I am embarrassed!"

"No, Lidia, don't be. I was glad to do it for you. I would be glad to do anything for you. I want to take care of you and your children for the rest of my life. I really do care for you deeply. I feel so sure that God is leading us together that I am willing to wait as long as it takes for you to say yes!"

Lidia turned to go in. "Thank you, Anton. I appreciate that deeply."

Two months later, Anton took his bride and her two children to his village. Fully recovered from his disease, and dismissed from the army because the war was over, he had prepared a small house for them. At their new home that first night, they knelt with the children and dedicated their house, their lives, and their future to their Lord and Savior, Jesus Christ.

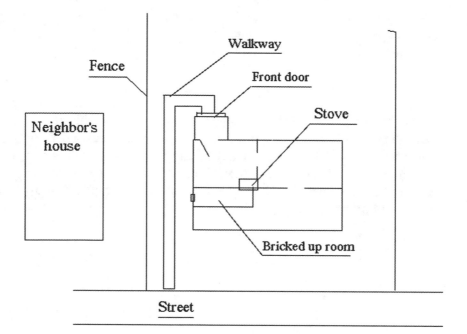

Fence

Walkway

Front door

Stove

Neighbor's
house

Bricked up room

Street

11

Bricked Up!

We were visiting with "Pavel" about the difficulties of the Christians in Ukraine during communist years when this interesting story surfaced. There were a number of things that Pavel forgot, but it was amazing how well he conveyed his inner feelings about what he and his friend endured being hidden while World War II swirled around them. Interestingly, many people in the villages did not know what really was happening, which government was in control, or if there still was a war. They only knew what was happening in their own village and, of course, had to deal with all the rumors that spread like an epidemic.

"Come in! Come in!" The green–painted, wooden door swung open wide to admit *Pavel*. His friend *Andrei* welcomed him inside.

"Hello! It is getting cold enough to snow!" *Pavel* hurried inside the humble, mud–brick house. With the door closed, the sharp wind could no longer numb him.

"Here! Have a cup of hot tea!" Andrei took the kettle from the back of the large masonry stove and poured out a stream of steaming liquid.

Pavel wrapped his fingers around the porcelain cup and sipped at the scalding liquid. The tea made a burning path down his throat, but it felt good. He glanced at the kitchen table.

Andrei followed his friend's glance. He shrugged one shoulder expressively. "Sorry, no sugar."

"That's all right. I forgot." Pavel grinned at Andrei. "We don't have sugar at our house, either. In fact, we don't even have tea!"

"Mama found this tea growing along the stream bank last summer," Andrei explained. "She came home and got the whole family to go with her and harvest it. It's been drying in the attic ever since."

The heat from the huge masonry stove began to warm Pavel. He untied the knitted muffler around his neck and unbuttoned several buttons from his heavy, woolen coat.

"Is your father still repairing your house walls?" Pavel asked as he heard the sound of tapping from the next room.

"Trying to. With all the unrest from the war, he had not been able to get any building materials for a long time, but several days ago he got a load of bricks from a man down by the river who had made some extra." Andrei rubbed his hands together, brushing away the dry mud from them.

"The war is coming closer," Pavel said between sips of hot tea. "I heard from our neighbor that the Germans have been in *Malin*, conscripting men and boys for the army. He thinks we need to be ready to hide whenever they sweep through here."

Both boys were silent as they thought of the terror that had been raging through Ukraine for the last three years.

"Let's go see what your father is doing," Pavel suggested. The two boys stepped into the adjoining pantry.

"Here comes more help!" Andrei's father greeted them cheerfully. He was mixing a plaster of brown mud in a large, flat pan. Bricks of the same color were stacked neatly along the outside wall.

"See, Papa is making a cold-storage room along this outside wall. The heat from the stove on the other side of this wall through the middle of the house will keep the new room from freezing. And the new wall will keep the pantry from getting as cold as it does now." Andrei led Pavel to the far end of the room and showed him the new storage place.

The doorway to the new enclosure was still wide open, and Andrei's father was preparing to lay the final bricks around the opening. Pavel looked into the long, narrow room. A small window, high in the short outside wall, gave light to the otherwise dark space.

While the boys were inspecting the new storage room, they heard the sound of running footsteps outside the house. Then, a frantic pounding at the door took them all into the front room.

"Brother *Ivan Nickolaevich*! The Germans are coming!" The middle—aged man panted out the news. "They are coming down the main road, not quite three kilometers from here! My son was out in the woods getting firewood when he saw them in the distance. He just came home and I ran right over to tell you!"

Andrei looked at Pavel in alarm. Both boys knew they were in immediate danger of being conscripted. Already, most of the young men in their village had been drafted into the Soviet army and were away fighting the Germans. Now, as the Germans were sweeping through the country, they were gathering up even younger men and pressing them into service as they moved northward into neighboring Russia.

"You must hide!" Ivan said as he looked at his son Andrei, and then at Pavel. "But where?"

"It is too risky to try to escape the village. You will be shot!" The message bearer said bluntly. "I must go and warn the others in the village."

"Yes, brother, go. And may God be with you!" Then Ivan briefly closed his eyes.

Pavel's heart began beating rapidly. He wished he was at home with his widowed mother. He knew she would be greatly concerned about his safety.

"Quickly! There is no time to spare," Brother Ivan spoke calmly, yet with conviction. "Get into the cold-storage room, and I will brick you inside."

"What?" Andrei asked incredulously.

But his father was already at work. He grabbed a brick, and, putting just a minimum amount of wet plaster on it, placed it in the narrow opening. Then another, and another.

Pavel understood what the elderly man had in mind. He moved a pile of bricks within the experienced brick layer's reach.

"I will get some blankets! It will be cold in there!" Andrei darted into the next room.

Before the doorway was bricked waist high, both boys stepped inside. The narrow opening became smaller and smaller until they could just see Ivan's head as he quickly, but methodically, placed brick after brick from side to side.

"God bless you! Be as quiet as possible and may the Lord protect you!" Then the last row of bricks was placed beneath the ceiling, and the door was completely closed off. The boys could hear the scrape of the metal trowel as excess plaster was scraped off the new wall.

Then, all was silent in the next room. "Your father must have gone to see what is happening," Pavel said to his friend. "I sure hope—and pray—that this works."

"Listen!" Andrei grabbed Pavel's arm. "I hear them coming!"

Though the small window was closed, the two boys could hear the sound of marching feet outside. Then a voice called out in German. The marching stopped.

The stream of German commands made no sense to Pavel's straining ears. "What are they saying?" he whispered to Andrei.

"I don't know! Oh, Pavel, we must pray! What if they find us here? They will surely shoot us if we refuse to bear arms and join their army! I—I try to prepare myself, but I don't know if I am ready!" Andrei's voice, even though hushed, quivered as he spoke.

There was a commotion in the street, just outside their new hiding place. Pavel could clearly hear the yard gate slam shut, then the sound of boots marching past their little window and around to the front of the house facing away from the street. The little house shuddered as the front door slammed against the wall. The sound of loud voices and stomping boots reached through the walls and into the storage room. Pavel could hear the questioning tones of the officers as they addressed Andrei's father in broken Russian.

Then the soldiers were in the pantry, right outside their hiding place. He could hear them walking about, kicking at the loose bricks and scuffing across the wooden floor.

Pavel felt his throat constrict. He tried taking slow, deep breaths. His heart pounded alarmingly loud.

Would they see that the bricks had just been laid? Could they see that the new wall did not match the one across from the door where they had come in? Could they tell that the pantry was not as long as the main room of the house?

Pavel felt exposed. In spite of the brick wall, he felt as though the searching men could see right into their hiding place and see both Andrei and himself hiding under the blankets in the corner of the room.

Watching the brick wall in the half–light, Pavel tried to prepare himself for the shouts of triumph when the first hole appeared.

"Lord! Help us!" Pavel's prayers went winging upward, his mind repeating a silent supplication to God.

He felt Andrei trembling beside him. He placed his hand on his friend's arm, and squeezed it slightly. He heard Andrei give a slight sigh.

When he heard thumping noises overhead, he did not know what was happening. Surely the soldiers were not tearing the house apart! They really did not know that the boys were hiding here, did they?

Then the noises overhead stopped, and he could hear the men in the room beside them again. They left the pantry and went into the main part of the house. Then, all was still.

"Did they leave?" Andrei breathed into Pavel's ear.

"I don't know," Pavel said, his mouth at Andrei's ear. "Don't talk! Pray!"

Andrei nodded his head. He shifted his legs to a more comfortable position.

The two boys had sunk to their knees as soon as they had heard the soldiers entering the house. Unconsciously they had taken this position as they huddled beneath the blankets for further protection.

Outside they heard the noise of the search continue. At times there was an outbreak of shouting from the soldiers. Sharp reports of rifle fire rang out. Screams of anguish tore through the village streets.

What was happening? The boys could only guess. Dread hung over them like a thick fog. Andrei began to shiver uncontrollably.

Pavel took one of the blankets and tried to wrap it more tightly around his friend. He huddled close beside him for warmth and comfort.

Through the entire day, the boys huddled in a corner of the storage room. Occasionally, they changed positions to relieve their cramped legs. But most of the time, they did not dare move. They felt safer staying in one spot. They had no idea how long the search would continue, nor if the house would be searched again.

When the early darkness of night extinguished the light that came through their tiny window, the boys welcomed it. They felt safer in the dark. They stood up cautiously, and even moved around inside the tiny space.

All night long the two boys huddled under the blankets, trying to stay warm. Pavel dozed off several times, only to jerk wide awake and lie staring into the darkness, trying to make sense of where he was. Then, his memory came back, and he felt fear begin to spread out deep inside him.

Sometimes Andrei woke up, too, with a start. Both boys would lie on the floorboards, trembling.

That night, they did not talk. There seemed to be nothing to say. The unknown lay ahead of them, huge and black and threatening.

When the winter morning at last sent its first rays of light through the window, both boys were sleeping. The long night had exhausted them. They lay side by side, covered by the thick blankets, getting as much body heat from each other as they could.

When Pavel woke up, he knew instantly where he was. He looked over at Andrei. He was still sleeping, his head almost completely hidden beneath his woolen cap. The blanket was pulled up around his neck.

Pavel began to pray. He could think more clearly now that daylight had come. The night had been full of terror, and he had not been able to put his prayers into words. Now he felt a calmness, an inner peace that settled over him like a comforting robe.

"Lord, I don't know what will happen to us, but if it be Your will, keep us hidden from the Germans. I want to be ready to suffer for You if You see best, but I am weak and I know I need to gather all my strength from You." Memories of the gunfire they had heard the day before came back to him. "I want to be faithful to You and be willing to give my life for the sake of the Gospel. Lord, I need

Your strength!"

Andrei stirred beside him, then sat up. His eyes were wide open as he took in their situation. "We are still safe!" he breathed in wonder.

"Yes," Pavel replied softly. "God has kept His angels watching over us all night long. Last night I didn't always feel the presence of the Lord, but this morning I have been blessed with knowing that God is with us."

Andrei was silent. He looked toward the window. "I wonder what is happening outside." He tossed the blankets aside and quietly stood to his feet. Then he walked over to the window.

"Can you see anything?" Pavel asked in a whisper as he joined Andrei.

Andrei moved slightly to one side so Pavel could see out. An old curtain hung in front of the window, partially obscuring the view. But even when Pavel pushed it aside, there was little to see.

The neighbor's house was directly across from the room they were in. The path to the front door led between the two houses. All the boys could see was a small patch of the neighbor's yard and the side of the house. Above it, they could see a portion of gray sky.

Outside, everything was still. Frost lay thickly on the naked branches of the fruit trees. Pavel saw a sparrow hop along the branches, fluffing his feathers. Even through the window, he could hear the twittering bird. Nothing else moved.

He stood on tiptoes to see if he could see anything more. He heard something crunch underfoot.

"What's here in the corner?" he asked quietly.

"Oh! I forgot!" Andrei replied, stooping and stretching out his hands toward where Pavel was standing. "This is where we had stored the sunflower seeds before Papa made the storage room. I wonder . . . I hope there are still some here!" Even in his excitement, he barely spoke above a whisper.

Pavel stooped and began exploring the corner too. He felt the little hard shells of the sunflowers. There was a whole pile!

Suddenly he realized how hungry he was. He had not eaten anything since he left home yesterday morning. How long ago that was!

Popping the seeds into his mouth, he expertly shelled and ate the tiny seeds. The good crunchy flavor was the first bright spot in this place.

Pavel looked around the storage room now that it was light. Narrow—he could reach out and touch both side walls at the same time—and twice as long as it was wide, the space was very confining. Like a prison cell.

"It's like being in jail. Only we have placed ourselves in here instead of someone else putting us in." Andrei must have been thinking along the same lines as Pavel.

"Plus, we have no idea how long we will be in here." Pavel had barely spoken when they heard noises outside the house.

It was obvious the Germans were still in the village. There were shouts and commands, not in Russian, and the sound of many feet marching over frozen ground. Sometimes the boys heard a dog barking wildly. If the barking continued, shots rang out and the barking stopped abruptly.

Pavel felt terror grab his insides. He hunkered down beside Andrei and they instinctively pulled the blankets over their heads.

Many times in his childhood, Pavel had played Hide–and–Seek with his friends. He had always enjoyed finding some obscure corner and holding perfectly still for long minutes at a time.

As a boy, he had somewhat enjoyed the feeling that crept over him as he realized his playmate was coming closer and closer. Pavel remembered how prickles of excitement always accompanied the moment just before discovery. The burst of emotion from having been found had both delighted and frightened him.

But this was no game. The feeling of being hunted was there, though. He knew the Germans were trying to make sure they did not miss any of the eligible young men of their village. They would search the houses more than once. He was almost sure of that.

The commotion outside faded away into the distance. He heard Andrei give a deep sigh.

All day long, they waited in their bricked–up hideout for something to happen. But there was no way of knowing what was going on. Intermittent shouts on the street and commotions outside let them know that the soldiers were still about.

Pavel and Andrei ate the sunflower seeds when all was silent outside. Until they got thirsty, that is.

Licking his lips, Pavel stared at the wooden floor. How long would they be in this hiding place? And what would they do for water? They could sustain themselves for a long time with the energy they derived from the sunflower seeds, but they needed water!

"I'm so thirsty!" he said to Andrei. "What are we going to do for water in here?"

Andrei must have been thinking the same thing. "Maybe my father will remember us and put a jug of water on the window sill. But I hope he will do it soon!"

But all that day, no one came to the house. The boys could tell that the house was empty, for never a sound did they hear all day. Where Andrei's parents were, they had no idea. They knew that many of the villagers had probably fled for safety and to avoid questioning by the Germans.

Their hunger grew as the day stretched on. But they did not munch on sunflower seeds anymore. It would just increase their thirst.

"I'm glad it is not summertime! I don't think I could make it this long without water if it was hot!" Andrei said in the evening. "Because it is cold, I don't feel as thirsty as I would if it were warm."

The boys still whispered whenever they talked to each other. They did not know whether or not a guard was stationed outside, watching for any sign of inhabitants hiding. For some reason, they still felt they were under surveillance.

After a night of relatively undisturbed sleep, the boys woke the next morning to find a soft luminous light pouring in through the little window.

"Snow!" Andrei exclaimed softly. "God sent us snow for water!"

It took a long time to open the window a crack at a time to make sure there was no sudden movement or noise that could be detected from outside. Then the boys took turns carefully taking handfuls of snow off the window ledge and filling their mouths with the welcome moisture. Again and again they reached out, until the ledge was bare. Snow continued to fall in huge flakes, insuring of more when they needed it.

After their thirst was quenched, they turned to the pile of sunflower seeds again. Now they ate with a keen appetite.

"When I prayed for water, I didn't think God would send snow!" Pavel marveled. "I kept praying that your parents would remember we were in here and would bring us water."

Andrei nodded. "I kept praying the same thing," he acknowledged. "I know that my father will never forget that we are here. If he is still alive," he added soberly.

Silence filled their little room. There was nothing to say.

The day passed uneventfully. Sitting side by side, the boys spent much of their time methodically placing sunflower seeds into their mouths and spitting out the hulls. The rapidly falling snow gave them all the water they needed whenever they became thirsty.

In the afternoon, they did sit-ups to relieve their caged feelings. They could even laugh at each other as they tried to see who could do the most sit-ups at one stretch. But they kept their laughter silent. They did not forget where they were.

The third day was much the same. But once, during the third night, it sounded as though someone was quietly moving around in the main room where the huge masonry stove stood silently. The boys held still as they put their ears against the wall and listened intently. Once they heard a muffled thump, then all was silent. After that, they heard nothing.

They stayed reasonably warm inside their layers of clothing and with the blankets. Sometimes if they pressed against the wall that separated them from the main room they could feel slight warmth emanating from the rough surface.

It was on the fourth day of their imprisonment that a loud noise outside woke them up. There were shouts and screams of protest. A woman's voice wailed and the faint sound of marching feet reached the listening pair inside the storage room. A prickle of fear ran up their scalps as heavy, booted footsteps went past the window. Again, the boys went through the agony of hearing someone in the house, apparently searching for any hidden people.

Pavel felt his stomach churn and he bent over, clutching his middle. Sweat beaded his forehead and he felt hot all over.

They could tell where the soldiers were looking by the sound of the booted feet. Again and again they came into the pantry just outside their hiding place.

Once, Pavel felt sure they were discovered. They heard a scraping noise, and then someone spoke right outside the newly bricked wall. The foreign words made no sense to the terrified boys, but the voice was near enough to set their already stressed hearts to racing even faster.

When the searchers finally left the house, the boys still did not feel safe. They could hear the voices of the soldiers as they searched in the barn. More than once, they walked right under the window of the cold-storage room.

Next, they heard them next door. Evidently, they were making a systematic search through the entire village.

Pavel felt sure it was the Lord who saved them. The Germans were accustomed to the many ruses the country folk used to evade the clutches of their army. They knew where to look. They knew what signs to look for to indicate that sons had been living in the houses.

What about his mother? Was she all right? Was she being tortured for information about the hiding place of her son? And Andrei's parents? Had they been willing to die rather than give any information about their whereabouts?

"Lord, it is so hard not to know what is happening! Sometimes I think I cannot bear it!" Wild thoughts of trying to break through the brick wall in the night to find out what was happening swept over him in his times of despair.

"What good would that do?" Andrei argued with him one night when they couldn't sleep. "Would it change our circumstances? What would you do? Try to fight against the entire German army?"

"No," Pavel admitted. "But not doing anything—not *knowing* anything—almost drives me to distraction!"

Other times it was Andrei who felt cooped up and wanted action of some kind. "I get so tired of nothing to eat except sunflower seeds!" he exploded the sixth day of their hiding. They had started marking on the wall every time another day ended. "If I could just have some bread, or potatoes, or milk!"

"Sure!" Pavel chuckled. "What about some chicken, or maybe a good hot bowl of *borscht*?"

They laughed ruefully.

For two days, they had hardly heard any sound of activity outside. Had the Germans left? Would it be safe now to batter down the walls into the next room and try to escape?

Why did Andrei's father not come? Surely he would not forget the two boys he had bricked up in his own house. Where were Andrei's parents?

"I think they cannot come," Andrei remarked gloomily. He reached under his cap and scratched vigorously.

Both boys were sitting on the blankets with their backs against the wall after their daily stint of pushups.

"There is heat coming from this wall!" Pavel whispered. "I don't know why, but this wall never gets completely cold!"

They both pressed their cheeks against the rough, plastered surface. Then they felt the adjoining wall. The short wall was definitely warmer!

"Someone is keeping a fire going in the stove!" Andrei's voice cracked with emotion. "Someone remembers that we are still in here!" He looked at his friend with wide eyes.

"Your father!" Pavel breathed.

"Then there is still danger, too! Or else he would get us out of here! The houses must be under watch all the time!"

"Remember the night we heard noises in your front room?" Pavel tried to piece the mystery together. "Your father must come at night to put wood on the fire."

"Wouldn't the watchman see the smoke from the chimney?" Andrei puzzled.

"No," Pavel shook his head. "You know if a slow fire is kept in our masonry stoves, there is almost no smoke at all coming from the chimneys. If he adds wood at night, by the next morning there would be no sign of smoke at all!"

"Then he is alive! Praise God!"

Andrei reached up under his cap again. "Something is biting me!" He jerked his cap off and ran his hand through his hair.

Pavel also felt something itching on his scalp. He reached up and scratched.

"Lice!" Andrei yelped. "The warmth we get from the wall is also bringing a nuisance!"

"Oh, no!" Pavel groaned. He immediately began scratching his head vigorously.

"Come to think of it," Andrei suddenly remembered, "our dog used to sleep in this corner in the winter. I wonder what happened to Belka anyway!"

Their cell, as they now called the room, had a definite lived-in odor. The boys had been forced to use a corner of their room as a latrine. Fortunately, a wide crack in the floorboards helped their situation. Though they kept that corner covered by an old rag they had found, their entire room still smelled quite much like an outhouse.

And now lice!

"See if you can see anything!" Pavel pleaded. He bent his head toward his friend.

Thus began the daily routine of searching for the vermin. If they relaxed their efforts to find the little biting critters, they would be tormented with itching.

It also gave them something to do. Time hung heavily as the days marched on.

Sometimes, they prayed together, or took turns telling stories they remembered from the Bible. They often talked about the worship services they used to attend.

"Too many times, I did not truly appreciate those times together," Pavel said ruefully one day as they ate some more sunflower seeds. It was better not to think of what they were eating anymore. Better just to eat and get nourishment. Better never to mind how tired they were of the same taste every day.

"I know what you mean," Andrei said. "But I am so thankful now for all the teaching we did hear. I don't know about you, but every promise from God is doubly meaningful now that I have nothing else secure."

Pavel got up to get some snow from the window. It was amazing how much it snowed! Perhaps for a day it might not snow, and the boys would begin to worry about their source of water. But before they would get desperately thirsty, it would snow again. Truly, it was a miracle from the Lord!

They were now in their second week of hiding. Twelve days. Though they had something to eat, by now there were times when they thought they could not eat sunflower seeds anymore. "I don't know how much longer I can survive this diet!" Andrei complained one morning. "Plus, the lice are driving me crazy! I haven't heard any Germans for the last three days now. Why don't we try to break down the wall and escape?"

Pavel heard the discouragement in his friend's voice. "Do you think it is safe? What if the Germans are still here and are waiting for anyone in hiding to come out? Surely your father would come and let us out if all danger was past!"

Andrei disagreed. "No! I don't think my father is even living anymore, or at least not free. He would never allow us to be shut up this long without letting us know that he is all right." He frowned and looked intently at the walls that imprisoned them. "I feel like taking something and bashing those bricks right out."

Pavel looked around the tiny room. "What would you use?"

There was nothing. The room was almost completely bare except for the pile of sunflower seeds and blankets.

Andrei scowled and looked at the floor. "Maybe we could pry up one of the floorboards and use that as a battering ram."

"But Andrei!" Pavel protested. "I don't think it is safe to try to get out. I know you think your father is no longer around, but remember, someone is keeping the fire going. Who else would it be besides your father? And I am almost sure that the Germans are still here. Please, let's wait a while longer."

Andrei stared at the floor. A deep furrow creased his forehead. Then he started scratching again.

"These lice! Can't you see where the nasty critters are?" He bent his shaggy head of black hair toward his fellow prisoner.

Pavel parted Andrei's hair and hunted. Distasteful as it was, they were always willing to go through the search for each other.

Head bent low, Andrei gave a rueful laugh. "I guess God knew we needed the lice to make us get along with each other. It is pretty hard to be angry with someone who is kind enough to pick lice out of your hair."

Pavel felt relieved. "I don't want to be stubborn, but I really feel we need to wait some more. It just doesn't seem as though the village is free yet."

It was on the fourteenth morning that they finally heard a familiar voice calling to them from outside the little window. "Andrei, my son! Pavel! Is all well with you?"

"Papa!" Andrei unrolled himself from the blanket and flew to the window. He swung the window wide open. "Papa! You have come!"

"Yes!" The boys could hear relief in the old man's voice. "The Russians have finally come and driven the Germans away! I'll come inside right away and let you out!"

With strong, sure strokes of his chisel and hammer, Ivan Nickolaevich opened the doorway. The boys eagerly helped remove the bricks as soon as they were loose.

Andrei was full of questions. "Why didn't you come to the window before? You could have let us know that you were all right!"

His father paused, with hammer in mid-air. He looked at the two boys peering at him through the small hole. "The Germans were stationed right across the street. They had a clear view of the path that goes to our front door. With all the snow, there was never an opportunity to come without leaving my tracks."

Andrei looked at Pavel. "They were so close! We never knew it!"

"Did you keep the fire going in the stove?" Pavel asked. "The wall never got cold and one night we thought we heard something fall."

Ivan chuckled. "I dropped a piece of firewood in the dark. Yes. I didn't want you to freeze."

The boys looked at each other as Ivan began prying the bricks loose again. They had not been forgotten, but watched for carefully all the time!

When the hole was big enough for the boys to squeeze through, they crawled out of their prison.

"Where is Mama?" Pavel asked as soon as he was out. "Is she all right?"

"Yes," the older man answered with emotion. "She is at the choir director's house. Go! She has been eagerly waiting for your release."

"Is there any danger of the Russians conscripting us?" Pavel could not shake the fear from his mind.

"My son," Ivan said simply. "Yes, there is danger as long as the war is on. We have been told that the war will soon be over. However, the same Lord who preserved you all those days in the storage room will be able to keep you from here on.

"Go in peace, and trust in the Lord!"

Free! At first, Pavel only walked rapidly toward the house where his mother was waiting. Then, he began to run down the snowy street.

12

Vera, Child of Faith

This is the story of a dear friend of ours. Through Vera, we have been able to meet many of the people featured in these books. Today, thirty-some years later, she still faithfully serves the Lord.

"Hurry, Vera!" Lucy urged, as she ran out of the kitchen. "It's almost time!"

Vera industriously scrubbed the frying pan. The scorched potato seemed to stick harder. She took a table knife and scraped at it. Finally, she got the stubborn spot clean.

With as much speed as a nine-year-old could muster, she wiped the top of the table clean, wiped the sink dry after the sudsy water was gone, and then dried her hands. With pigtails flying, she dashed out of the little kitchen and scampered down the hall.

"Whoa!" Vera's papa laughed as she crashed into him. "Slow down! There is still time!"

By the time she got into the living room, the others were already gathered in expectancy, either on the cot that served as a couch by day and a bed by night, or on the floor. Vera plopped breathlessly on the rug beside her sister Lucy.

Her cousins, *Sveta* and *Tamara*, were eagerly waiting on the cot with *Volodya*, Vera's older brother. Even her little brother *Vanya*, only four years old, wiggled in excitement.

"Shh!" Volodya cautioned, fiddling with the dials on the brown radio cabinet. "It's almost time! One more minute!"

159

The children, none of whom were older than fourteen, quit shifting about. Sveta lifted her finger to her lips, smiling at Vanya who gave a little hitch of excitement on the cot.

"Good evening to all my listeners!" a man's pleasant voice announced in Russian. "I greet you in the name of Jesus Christ, the living Son of God! Welcome to our Children's Bible Program. The Gospel Program will follow this program in thirty minutes. Please stay tuned for one hour of Christian teaching and singing! And now, we are ready for Aunt *Tanya* to begin her story for the evening."

Vera moved her leg to a more comfortable position. Tonight the reception was good. Sometimes the broadcast from Monte Carlo (in Monaco, France) was plagued with static and brief interruptions, but this evening the cold Ukrainian air outside their house must be an excellent conductor for the radio waves.

"Good evening, children!" A lady's kind voice spoke warmly from the speakers.

"Good evening, Aunt Tanya!" The listening children echoed, laughing softly. Vera could see her mother, standing just outside the living room door, laughing with them.

This was a regular custom for as long as the program had been going. Answering the greeting was just one more link to the outside world, a world they could only dream about. But the most special thing of all was that on the radio, Christians presented a program for them! A program in Russian, beamed at all the Russian-speaking countries in Eastern Europe! What a treat!

"This evening I want to tell you about a boy who trusted in the Lord, even when all the grown-up men were afraid. The boy's name is David.

"David grew up in the hill country and took care of his father's sheep. He learned to sing and he spent many days playing on his harp. He loved to watch over the sheep and be their shepherd.

"But not all was pleasant! Sometimes wild animals attacked the flock!"

Vera knew the story well. All of them knew the Bible story of David, the shepherd boy of Israel. Even little Vanya knew it.

But not a sound did they make through the entire telling of the story of David and Goliath. Aunt Tanya kept them spell-bound by her narration, using expression to illustrate the story for her listeners.

When she told the part of Goliath roaring at the young lad, her voice filled the village house. Vanya covered his ears and shut his eyes.

"I come in the name of the Lord God of Israel!" They could hear the confidence and trust in the words as Aunt Tanya changed her voice to imitate a young boy.

And when the Philistines were put to flight and David was hailed as a hero, Aunt Tanya seized the moment to plant faith in the hearts of all the listeners.

"The same God David served is still alive today! He is the Creator of heaven and earth and is watching over the entire world. He is still looking for boys and girls and men and women who put their trust and confidence in Him. If we believe in God and have faith in His power, wonderful things can still happen to us!

"You can start anytime! Right now you can talk to God and ask Him to give you faith in Him. He hears every word you say! He knows how you feel deep down inside your heart. And the most wonderful thing of all is that He loves you!"

Vera had the same feeling she had whenever they gathered for worship. A feeling of wonder and a thrill of knowing that God loved everyone. Loved her! She looked at her cousins and at her brothers and Lucy. A warm glow spread throughout her entire body. God loved them all!

"What can you do to serve God?" Aunt Tanya's voice went on. "You can be an obedient child and obey your parents. You can be kind and loving to your brothers and sisters. You can help the old people in your village. All these things are a way of showing that you love God and that you are trying to serve Him the best that you can.

"Believe in the Lord Jesus Christ to forgive your sins! He came to earth to give His life so that we can have our sins forgiven! He rose from the dead so that we who believe in Him can someday be with Him in heaven!

"Another important thing to help you is to read your Bible! If you can, read it every day!"

"We don't even have a Bible in our house!" Tamara interrupted.

"Shh!" her sister reminded. "Listen!"

"Perhaps you don't have a Bible of your own," Aunt Tanya's voice continued. "If you would like to receive a Bible of your very own, you may write to us and we will try to send you one."

The children in the room looked doubtfully at each other. How could that be possible?

"Maybe you think such a thing could not happen. You may wonder how, in your country, you could get your very own Bible in the mail. Well, here is a time for you to test your faith. If you ask God to make it possible, He may reward your faith by sending you one!"

"It would have to be God," Volodya said firmly. "Our government would never let Bibles come across the border by mail."

"I will give you the address," Aunt Tanya announced. "Here it is."

Vera had scrambled to her feet and grabbed a pencil from the desk. She smoothed a piece of paper expectantly. Then she carefully wrote every word of the address.

"This concludes the Children's Pro . . ." With a squawk, the announcer's voice was cut off and a loud jarring hum filled the room.

"Turn it off!" Lucy begged.

Volodya twirled the dial and the noise faded away. "Got scrambled again," he said with resignation.

"Are you going to write?" Sveta asked, reading the address on Vera's paper.

"Yes," Vera nodded her head emphatically.

"It won't be of any use," Lucy told her kindly. "Your letter would not even be allowed to leave our country, much less a Bible allowed to cross over the border."

"That's right," Tamara answered. "I don't think it would be worth the effort."

Vera had already gotten a clean sheet of paper.

"Mama!" Volodya raised his voice. When she appeared in the doorway he told her, "Vera wants to write to Aunt Tanya and ask for a Bible!"

Vera's mother came over and looked at the address her daughter had written down. "I don't think it will do any good," she said doubtfully, shaking her head. "I can't imagine that the government will let any letters go out to Monte Carlo, much less a Bible come through the mail to us. We believers all know that Bibles from abroad are considered contraband."

"That's what we told her," Lucy said nodding her head.

"Mother, please!" Vera looked pleadingly at her mother. "Aunt Tanya said that we should do this in faith. She said that God can send us a Bible!"

All eyes turned to see what Mother's response would be. Vanya grabbed his mother's hand. "I want to write, too! I want a Bible!"

"Yes, Vanya. We all would love to have a Bible of our own," Lucy laughed at her little brother.

"You may write letters if you want," Mother said softly. "I don't want to discourage anyone's faith. Perhaps God will open the doors and let you children get Bibles of your very own. That would be wonderful!"

"I'm going to write, too!" Sveta decided. "May I, Auntie?"

"Yes, write as many letters as you want. God can still do miracles!"

"I'll write, too," Tamara decided. "Lucy, you write one."

"OK." Lucy shrugged her shoulders and laughed. "I'll write one, too."

"I'll write one when your Bibles come," Volodya laughed. He started tickling Vanya under the arms.

While the two boys tussled on the floor, the girls each wrote a letter. Vera wrote:

> Dear Aunt Tanya,
>   I am a girl living in Ukraine. I would please like to have a Bible for my very own. I love Jesus very much. I love to listen to your program.

> Vera *Prelepa*

Underneath her name she printed her address very plainly. Then she copied Aunt Tanya's address on the outside of the envelope and inserted her letter. She sealed the envelope.

"Wait," Lucy said as she saw Vera seal the envelope. "We want to put our letters in, too."

"No," Mother interrupted, "let each one put their letter in separate envelopes. I think there will be a greater chance that your letters will get across the border that way. I shouldn't say 'chance' for God's hand does not do things by chance," she corrected herself. "But, let's try it that way."

"Let's ask God to bless our letters," Vera said after all the envelopes were addressed. "I have never gotten a package from any other country. But I know God can do it."

The four girls knelt on the floor of the little village house. In simplicity they asked God to guide the letters to Aunt Tanya's address. Then, they asked God to grant their request for a Bible.

"There! Now we have done all we can," Lucy said as they rose from their knees. "We will see if the Lord wants us to get a Bible or not."

Four letters with Aunt Tanya's address were lined up on the hall table, ready to be carried to the post office the next day. Four envelopes with identical requests. Four requests for Bibles.

That night, after her cousins had left and she was in bed, Vera prayed again. "God, I do want to serve You! I give my life to You as a willing servant. And please, God, if it be possible, send me a Bible! A Bible of my very own!"

In childlike faith, Vera prayed. Prayed for a Bible. Prayed for a miracle.

———————————

"Whew, it is hot already!" Sveta said, licking her lips to moisten them. "The sun just beats down on us and it's only the beginning of summer."

"You know how our Ukrainian summers are," Lucy laughed. "They start so suddenly. The weather just goes from chilly to hot overnight."

The four girls were on their way home from church. Today, they had gathered in Kiev in a believer's apartment for the Sunday service. The girls were walking down the sidewalk, headed for the bus stop.

"It will be hotter on the bus," Tamara sighed. "Come, Vera, don't drag behind so."

Vera quickened her steps. It would help if she could get a drink.

But she knew she would have to wait until they reached home, which was about a thirty-minute bus ride away.

"Whew! This feels better!" Lucy exclaimed, stepping into the shadow of a large building. "It makes a big difference to walk in the shade for a while!"

"The hospital is to make people feel better!" Sveta laughed. "Now the hospital makes us feel better by giving us shade."

"Thank you!" Vera said gratefully to the tall building on their right. "Thank you for shading us from the sun!"

A young man in his twenties came walking briskly toward them. He stared at the adolescent girls for a moment, then approached them.

"Excuse me," he said politely. "Do you know a . . ." he hesitated and then looked at his parcel, ". . . Vera Prelepa?"

Vera opened her mouth in amazement. She looked at Lucy, then back at the young man.

"Do any of you know Vera Prelepa?" he asked again.

"Yes." Lucy responded. "This is my sister." She reached for Vera's hand and looked wonderingly at her younger sister.

The young man followed her glance. He looked directly at Vera. "I have a parcel here for Vera Prelepa. Are you Vera?"

Vera could barely answer. She was so astonished! Who could possibly be sending her a package?

"Here. This is for you." He handed the parcel to her.

"Thank you!" Vera managed to say as the man turned to leave.

"What is it?" The three older girls crowded around Vera.

Vera felt the package. It felt like a book.

"Look!" Sveta exclaimed. "It has your name and address right on it!"

Vera looked in awe at her name. Yes, there in bold letters, it said "Vera Prelepa." It really was for her.

"Maybe there is another person with the same name," Tamara suggested. "Do you have any relatives with that name?"

"No," Lucy answered firmly.

"Shall I open it now or wait until later?" Vera wondered.

"Open it now!" Sveta said eagerly. The other two girls chimed in, "Yes, do! Open it now!"

A street-side bench made an excellent place to sit down and

open the parcel. Vera tore at the tape encircling the brown paper package.

"A Bible!" Vera said in awe as she reached inside and drew out a small Bible with a green cover. "*Biblia*" was stamped in gold on the spine.

"Shh!" Lucy warned as she looked up and down the sidewalk. "Vera, put it away until we get home!"

"Come girls, we must hurry or we will have to wait until the next bus comes."

Still slightly dazed by the wondrous happening, Vera followed the others. Her mind was in a whirl.

"Mother!" Lucy called as she and Vera entered their house, their cousins close behind them. "Come quickly!"

In a moment, their mother came hurrying from the kitchen. "What is it?" she asked, hearing the excitement in her daughter's voice.

"Mother! Vera got a package with a Bible!" Lucy exclaimed.

"Vera! Oh, Vera! Where is it?"

Vera held up her precious parcel to show her mother. "Look, Mother! I really did get a Bible!" She drew the wondrous Bible out of the parcel, and carefully turned the pages.

"It smells brand new!" Sveta marveled softly.

"It is new!" Mother said. "Here, daughter, may I see it?"

Vera gave the Bible to her mother. Her heart was still beating fast from all the excitement.

"Who sent it?" Sveta asked. "Do you think it was from Aunt Tanya?"

"Yes," Vera replied, "I think this Bible came as an answer to the letter I wrote to Aunt Tanya. Remember, Mother, when we wrote the letters?"

"Yes, of course. Surely that is where it came from. God answered your prayers, little daughter of *faith*!"

The three other girls laughed. For *Vera* in Russian means *faith*.

"Well, I guess that explains why none of the rest of us got a Bible," Lucy said, looking longingly at her sister's Bible.

"Why just Vera?" Sveta wondered. "Why did just one Bible

come? We all four asked for Bibles. Why did they send just one?"

"Girls," Mother said seriously. "I don't know. It could easily be that only one letter somehow made it out of the country. I am surprised that Vera's letter ever reached its destination. Somehow it must have slipped through the border. It could have been stuck to another piece of mail and escaped by mistake. But really, I believe it made it because God designed it to get through."

"Wow!" Lucy looked at the Bible in Mother's hands. "Just think, someone actually got Vera's letter and sent this Bible to her."

"It was something special that made the letter get to Monte Carlo," Tamara said slowly, "but I think it is a miracle that the Bible ever got into our country, and a greater miracle that it ever arrived here safely."

"Who gave it to you?" Mother asked, looking tenderly at Vera.

"A young—" Lucy started.

"Lucy, I asked Vera," Mother shushed her oldest daughter.

"It was a young man," Vera said. "I don't know who he was. He just came to us by the hospital in the city and asked if we knew a Vera Prelepa." She grinned again at the memory. "Lucy told him that was me. So, he gave me the package. I don't even know where he went after that. I—I didn't think to look."

"Did he tell you his name?" Mother wondered. She looked at the other girls. "Do any of you know who he was?"

They all shook their heads.

"I didn't think about that," Vera said again. "I was so surprised to get a parcel, that I never even thought about who gave it."

"That is strange," Mother mused. "Someone who must have known our family. Of course, our address is written plainly on the front. But still, it is a highly unusual happening. A miracle, really!"

"May I write my name inside, Mother?" Vera asked eagerly. She looked up at her mother with sparkling blue eyes.

"Are you going to let her keep it for her very own?" Sveta wondered.

Vera looked at Sveta, then back to her mother. She swallowed and blinked her eyes.

"Certainly!" Mother's quick answer reassured Vera. "It is her Bible! It came with her name on the package. Here, let's take it to the desk and you can carefully write your name and the date inside the front cover."

Vera wrote as neatly as she possibly could. *Vera Prelepa. June 1964.* She carefully closed the Bible and hugged it to her chest.

Mother led them in a prayer. "Thank You, God, for answering Vera's prayer and sending this Bible to her. We thank You for creating this miracle to strengthen our faith. Bless Aunt Tanya for sending it to her. Bless all those who helped bring it to Vera. Lord, we are not worthy of Your care and love, yet You graciously allow us to receive Your rich blessings. Thank You, Lord Jesus!"

Vera's prayer was simple. "Thank You, God, for sending me this Bible. I want to obey it and serve You all my life."

The Bible was placed in a safe hiding place in the blanket chest. Too often, their home had been searched for contraband literature, as the government labeled any books or pamphlets not published in their country. Vera was used to hiding anything religious.

"Now we have two Bibles in the house," Lucy said. "But Vera's is smaller than our old one."

"Yes," Mother agreed. "Perhaps there will come a time when we can each openly have a Bible. Perhaps God will grant us that freedom someday!"

The girls looked at each other. What an astonishing idea! They could not imagine anything like that! All their lives, Bibles had been something to be hidden, something hard to obtain.

"Maybe we should all change our names to Vera. Maybe it would happen then!" Tamara said. They all laughed.

Vera treasured her Bible during all her growing-up years. When Mother's prophetic words finally came to fruition in the late 1980s and freedom came to Ukraine, Vera's Bible was almost completely worn out. But all through Vera's life, the miracle of her first Bible was a constant source of strength to the "child of faith."

13

The Food Parcel

In the early 1980s, Elena Boghian Marza (CAM staff member) collected addresses of poor Christian families from pastors in Romania. To help such families back then, the only way CAM could send food parcels and other items from America was through the communist government-controlled transportation system. This gave CAM less control and afforded greater potential for dishonest officials to remove items. The following story is based on my visit to this couple's home in 2001. With true gratefulness, "Angelica" told about her experience of how God blessed them so many years ago.

Morning daylight steals across the wintry landscape. The sky is the color of gray wool, stretched across the flat fields and woven into the horizon, where it meets the gray of the late winter snow. Smoke rises from scores of chimneys as breakfast fires are ignited and households stir into somnolent winter morning activities.

The filtered light entering a whitewashed cottage gradually illuminates a cot with sleeping children. It appears there are four, though it is difficult to tell as the mound under the heavy covers looks like a single unit. A woman in her mid-thirties is methodically stirring some gruel on the stove top.

Ana has four children. The oldest, Angelica, is nine. The two boys, Sami and *Beniamin*, are scarcely a year apart. *Elena*, the baby of the family, is two years old. Ana's husband is working in the coal mines in western Romania.

"Mama! I want a drink!" The weak voice calling from the bed is Angelica's.

Ana leaves the stove and goes into the kitchen. She returns with a glass of water and as Angelica sits up, lifts the glass to her lips.

"Are you hot?" Ana asks tenderly.

"Yes!" Angelica says, pushing the covers away from her.

"But you must not be chilled!" Ana pulls up a blanket around her daughter.

Angelica lies down again and closes her eyes.

Ana stands staring at her daughter. Then she turns back to the stove. Tears glisten in the corners of the mother's eyes as she thoughtfully stirs the cooking corn mush, *mamaliga.*

They eat breakfast this morning without Angelica. Their breakfast is only the mamaliga that Ana has just cooked. Nothing else. No milk or sugar for the mamaliga. No bread. No tea.

But the children eat the cooked cereal without complaining. In fact, they scrape the bottoms of their bowls over and over with their spoons, eating every last particle they can scrape up.

Ana gives the last of the cereal to Elena. She carefully scrapes the cooked mush from the corners of the baby's mouth. Her own mouth works unconsciously as she watches the food disappear.

"Angelica, dear, is there anything I can get for you?" Little lines of worry crease Ana's forehead.

"No, Mama," Angelica replies weakly. She manages a wan smile, then closes her eyes again.

"Sami." Ana speaks rapidly to her five-year-old son. "Mama has to leave for some time. Watch Elena so she does not get too near the stove. Don't go outside and if someone comes to the door, don't open it!" She looks intently down into his face and then reaches for her heavy coat.

The door closes behind the mother, and the four children are left alone in the little house. Sami lifts Elena up to the window and they watch their mother walk over the snowy path to the street. After Ana goes through the wooden gate, they can no longer see her.

Sami pulls out a cardboard box from under the bed where

Angelica is lying. He hands a bottle cap to Beniamin and one to Elena. Then he takes two more out of the box and gives them to the waiting hands. They begin to pile them up into a tower, each taking a turn. The soft breathing from Angelica on the bed and the tinkle of the jar lids are the only noise in the room.

"Mrs. *Simionescu,* is there anything I can do to earn some money? Or could I do some kind of work in exchange for some meat? My Angelica is sick and I would like to give her some meat broth to give her strength. For two weeks she has lain ill and it seems every day she gets weaker. Please! Is there some work I could do for you?"

It is Ana. She is in front of one of the village's largest homes. The Simionescu family even has the luxury of a separate bedroom for each of their three children!

Mrs. Simionescu looks at Ana from the entrance door. Her eyes rest briefly on the begging woman's face, then looks at the thin hands clutching the front of her coat together.

"*Petru* still at the mines?"

Ana nods.

"Come in." Ana steps inside. Her eyes never leave the other woman's face.

Three hours later, Ana, clutching a package wrapped in brown paper, closes the door of the Simionescu house and hurries down the front sidewalk.

After pushing open the front gate, her slight figure actually runs the last few steps. Her numb fingers fumble at the doorknob, then she pushes open the door and enters breathlessly. Closing the door behind her, she steps quietly through the little entry, through the kitchen, and into the main room of the house.

"Mama!" Elena lifts her arms in a glad welcome. Sami and Beniamin run to their mother, eagerly eyeing the package.

Ana hungrily reaches for the little ones. Then, she walks over to Angelica.

Her oldest daughter is still lying white and still on the cot. Ana smiles at her and gently rests her hand on Angelica's hair, careful not to touch Angelica's skin with her cold hand.

"I have brought you something that will give you strength, Angelica! Mrs. Simionescu gave us half a chicken!"

Four pairs of eyes hungrily look at the paper parcel. As Ana unwraps the package, Beniamin and Sami lick their lips. Elena reaches out a small hand.

"Wait!" Ana says gently, pushing the hand away. "I will cook it on the stove and add some potatoes to it. Maybe we can cook some carrots with it too and make a good soup for Angelica. Would you like that?" She looks at Angelica.

Angelica nods her head, her hair making a brushing noise against the pillow case.

The aroma of the cooking stew permeates every part of the little house. The children no longer play, but stand in front of the stove.

Even Angelica, supported by pillows, sits up in bed. Only her large brown eyes move, observing as Ana keeps a diligent watch over the simmering soup.

The three little children crowd around their mother as Ana slowly dips some of the hot broth into a bowl. All eyes watch as the mother blows gently across the steaming soup.

"Now, Angelica. Eat all you want!"

Holding the spoon with her white hand, Angelica dips again and again into the bowl. At every scoop of the spoon, four pairs of eyes watch the journey of the spoon from the bowl to the mouth. From Elena's baby mouth, a tiny pink tongue flicks out and licks her lips.

"Do you want more?" Ana asks as soon as the bowl is empty.

Angelica looks at her mother. "You eat some first." Her eyes look at each one of her siblings in turn.

"Angelica, you must eat to gain strength! Eat all you want!" Ana's voice trembles slightly.

"I want you to give some to the other children, Mama. And I want you to eat some too," Angelica insists.

Ana glances at the pot on the stove. Then she looks at the thin faces of her boys. Only Elena's face has the chubby cheeks of a baby.

"Sami, get some bowls. We will each have a little. The rest we must save for Angelica. For later!"

Elena squeals excitedly. The boys scamper to the kitchen.

"Wait, children! We will bow our heads and thank our loving Father for giving us this food. We will thank Him for His love." Ana takes Elena on her lap, and bends her neck. The little boys close their eyes and clasp their hands in prayer. Only Elena keeps her eyes open, looking at the pot of soup on the table.

The woman kneeling in the early morning light is Ana. She is praying silently, hardly moving her slight body. The children are sleeping together beneath the heavy covers.

Finally, Ana rises to her feet, glances at the children, and leaves the room. Soon she is back with a kettle of water which she places on the stove top.

"How are you feeling, Angelica?" she asks as she sees her daughter's eyes following her.

"I am better, I think," Angelica smiles back.

Sami sits up in bed, yawning and stretching his arms above his head. Little Elena, roused by the voices, sits up, too. Beniamin opens his eyes, but stays lying down.

As soon as the water boils, Ana pours in some cornmeal. She stirs the hot water briskly, scraping the bottom of the pot with her wooden spoon.

A noise outside arrests Ana's attention. She lifts her head from the task at hand and looks out the window.

The children hear the noise of the marching boots, too. As the door bursts open, they cower under the cover, only their large dark eyes peering out.

"Where is your husband?" The question is loud in the otherwise silent room. The questioner, a burly policeman, addresses Ana with a commanding tone.

Ana's hand flies up to her throat. "He—he is working in the mines," she falters. Her eyes dart from the policeman to the children. She sidles toward the bed.

"He has not been home for a long time?" The next question is asked in a milder tone. The officer looks at the children huddled under the covers. His encompassing eyes take in the cooking pot of mamaliga on the stove. He sees the small table set with only bowls and spoons.

"No," Ana answers simply.

"Lady, I feel sorry for you. If it were not for your fanatical beliefs, you could enjoy a normal life. Your husband could be teaching at the public school instead of laboring in the wretched mines. Why do you persist in clinging to your beliefs?"

Ana closes her eyes a moment then answers clearly. "We believe that the hard times we must endure because of our faith in Christ will be as nothing compared to the joyful future God has prepared for us in heaven. The Bible tells us that all those who live Godly lives shall suffer persecution. We are willing to suffer for the name of Christ."

The officer looks at the children, then shakes his head. "You must have a strong faith to let your children suffer for lack of food. Not many mothers would endure this."

Ana does not reply. She looks at the officer, then back again to her children.

After the officer has gone, Ana sighs a deep sigh. She turns to the children. "Come, it is time to eat."

Silently, all the children, except for Angelica, crawl out from under the covers and gather around the table. Ana spoons some porridge into a bowl and hands it to her oldest daughter.

With trembling lips, Ana prays over the meal.

The children eat rapidly. Soon, the pot is empty. Ana's bowl is still clean.

The big cardboard box sits on the end of the cot. Angelica is sitting next to it, staring at the box with wide eyes. The three little children crawl up on the cot, reaching out and touching the brown sides. Ana is trembling as she lifts the lid of the opened box.

The first thing the family sees is smaller packages inside. Food packages!

Ana reaches inside and lifts out a white package. The outside has a picture of a golden loaf of bread. Words in a strange language are written on it. "Wheat flour!" Ana says in wonder.

Nestled side by side lie three more packages. As she lifts each one out, Ana studies the front, and then says, "Rice! Sugar! Oats!" Two more packages make her brow wrinkle up, but then she sets the packages aside and digs deeper.

A white paper with words written in Romanian is taped to the inside of the box. Ana carefully loosens the paper and studies it for a moment. Her eyes open wider as she reads the list.

"Here!" she hands the list to Angelica. "You read to us what all is in this box!" Tears moisten her cheeks as she shakes her head and continues to dig deeper into the box.

Angelica stares at the paper for a moment, then reads in a husky voice. "Flour, rice, oat flakes, sugar, powdered milk, grits, yeast, coffee, cocoa, chocolate bars, beef bouillon, vegetable mix, vitamins."

A sound from Ana brings a pause to Angelica's reading. She looks up at her mother's face. She sees the tears streaming down over Ana's cheeks as she continues to lift packages from the box, her hands shaking. When she finds the bottle of vitamins, she lifts them toward the ceiling for a moment with eyes closed.

Angelica returns to the list. "Canned pork, canned beef, ham, liverwurst, bologna, salami, cheese, olive oil." Then she turns the paper over. Something is written there.

"Look, Mama! What does this say?"

Ana wipes her eyes and takes the paper. She studies the printed words of another language. "David," she reads out loud, fumbling over the unfamiliar English letters. "P, O, Box 52, Millersburg, Ohio."

Beniamin and Sami are stroking the packages, looking at the bright labels on some of the parcels. Elena is staring silently at the pile of food. Occasionally, her eyes dart to the box, then back to the food again.

Ana studies the list. Then she looks inside the box. She moves some of the cans on the table and studies the list again. Then, with a little shrug, she gives the paper back to Angelica.

"Where is the salami, Mama?" A wistful tone has crept into Angelica's voice.

"Um, I don't see it. The bologna, the salami, the cheese, and the liverwurst are missing."

"Who took it?" Sami asks bluntly.

"I don't know," Ana admits. "Children, this package is from God. He has seen our need and sent this to feed us. Come, let us gather around Angelica and thank Him. I want each one of you to thank God for sending this package to us. Thank Him for the kind people who are willing to share with us."

The slight form of the woman is still trembling as she kneels beside the cot. Her tears continue to course down her cheeks as they all give thanks. She leads little Elena in her prayer, then Sami and Beniamin pray. Angelica prays, and then Ana prays.

In less than an hour, delightful smells draw the children to the stove and they stare in wonder at the miracle before them. No one leaves the stove, and Ana does not shoo them away from underfoot.

At suppertime each plate is filled with a miracle: hot, steaming rice, and gravy made from an opened tin of beef. In front of each plate is a glass of hot cocoa, made with the powdered milk. Angelica is sitting at the table. Beside her plate are three vitamins. Her cheeks are flushed and her eyes sparkle.

Silently, Ana bows her head. The children follow her example. Once more, they offer fervent prayers of thanksgiving.

It is obvious the children can hardly restrain themselves after the prayer. Elena does not even try.

With trembling hands she quickly spoons the food into her mouth. Grains of rice dribble from her mouth, and Ana scrapes them up with her own spoon.

Beniamin eats rapidly at first, and then slows down. He looks at the food on his plate and then at the other plates.

Sami eats slowly. He carefully chews and swallows each mouthful. He pushes the rice into a little mound and then carefully scoops some onto his spoon. Almost with reverence he sips some of the hot cocoa.

Angelica, too, eats slowly. She places some of the gravy on a spoonful of rice then lifts it to her mouth. With her tongue, she pushes the food from side to side, then chews it thoroughly. After the first several mouthfuls, she gives a little sigh and looks at her mother.

Ana smiles a trembling smile. In turn, she looks at each of the children. Then, her eyes rest on the box, still on the bed. She glances once more at the children, silently eating their food.

Finally, she herself begins to eat. Over and over, she wipes her eyes. There are times when she closes her eyes for long moments, then once more looks at her children eating their food.

The long winter continues. At irregular intervals, the boxes arrive. Sometimes Ana finds over half of the contents removed. Sometimes there is almost nothing left in the box.

But no matter how much or how little they receive, Ana never fails in one thing. Always, every time a parcel arrives, she does the same thing. She gathers the children around and they give thanks to God for the food He has sent them. She does not complain about what they do not get. She does not speak about the people who remove some of the contents for their own use. She gives thanks to God for what He has allowed to come to their house to keep them from starving. Her grateful heart pours out in praise for the tender mercy of God to provide for them in their great need. And always, she thanks God for the caring people who have sent the food.

14

The Cost Of Salvation

This story was told to me by the pastor himself so I wrote it in first person. It must have happened around twenty years ago.

"Oh, I'm so glad you came!" The lady at the door welcomed us eagerly. "We have been waiting for you!"

Brother *Iosif* and I stepped inside. We slipped off our shoes in the front entry, and Lavinia gave us felt house slippers to wear.

"Come right this way. My husband and daughter are waiting for you." Lavinia bustled us into the living room. We sat down on the narrow cot. I placed my briefcase on the floor beside me and exchanged pleasantries with *Valer*, Lavinia's husband.

"Pastor Victor," Lavinia began immediately, looking at me, "I want you to hear my story."

"Yes," I replied, "I've been wondering why you invited us here."

Lavinia glanced at her daughter before she began speaking. "Actually, it is because of *Lamaita*. She is only eleven years old, but it was she who first began all this.

"She read a little book that she got somewhere. It was about hell and the people who go there. It really frightened her and she talked about it all the time. Every morning, the first thing she would do when she got up was tell Valer and me that if we don't all repent from our sins, we will all go to hell. Isn't that right, Lamaita?"

Troubled brown eyes looked directly at us. Lamaita nodded her head in assent. "I'm scared of hell," she admitted.

"Well," her mother went on, "she got me scared too. Lamaita no longer had the little book, so we could not read it, but still she kept insisting that we need to do something or we will go to hell when we die. Like I said before, I became afraid too. I talked to Valer about it and, at first, he said we shouldn't worry about it.

"But Lamaita would not give up. She began asking neighbors if they know how to keep from going to hell. She wanted me to ask the priest, but I could never get him to listen to what I said. I know I talk a lot, but I do need answers about this.

"Finally one of our neighbors said they had heard about your church in *Piatra Neamt*, a little distance away. So one Sunday Lamaita and I came to your church. That is when we asked you to come here and teach us how to stay out of hell."

I prayed for wisdom and guidance. Truly, this woman and her daughter were seeking for truth. I was not too sure about Valer yet. He seemed more detached.

I remembered well their visit to our small church. After the message, I had been surprised to see a woman stand up and address us. She had introduced herself and her daughter, and told us she was from the village of *Gircina*. She said they came seeking for a way to stay out of hell. Then, abruptly, she had sat down again. I had told her then that we would be glad to help her in any way we could. After the service, Brother Iosif and I had met with her. She had invited us to come to her home, so now, the following Tuesday, here we were.

All eyes were on me as I began to speak. "Truly, I can see that God has moved through your daughter, Lamaita, to make you seek for the truth. Seeking is the first step toward God. In the Bible," I opened my case and got out my Bible, "it says that God 'is a rewarder of them that diligently seek him.' God will never turn away a truly seeking heart."

With Brother Iosif's help, I told our listeners the wonderful story of how Jesus had come to earth. Though they were familiar with the birth, death, and resurrection of Christ, it was obvious they had only a shallow understanding of Him.

Lavinia and her daughter drank up every word we were saying. I knew Valer was listening intently, too, but he did not show quite the eagerness to understand as did the other two. I began praying that the truth would penetrate his heart also.

While we explained how we must repent, not only from our sins, but also from our sinful inclinations, I noticed tears forming in Lavinia's eyes. I could tell she was burdened with the weight of her sins. Lamaita, too, seemed deeply moved.

For two hours we spoke and answered their many questions. Valer had almost nothing to say, yet listened keenly.

Even though we were getting the most response from his wife, it was to Valer that I addressed the question. "Valer, do you want to give your life to Jesus? Do you want to find forgiveness from your sins and have peace with God in your heart?"

From beneath his shaggy eyebrows he looked soberly at me, and yet did not say anything.

"Oh, Valer!" Lavinia broke in. "Don't you want to join us? I want to be saved! Oh, I must be saved! Lamaita, come join Mama and we will pray with these men." In her agitation, she knelt on the carpet, her daughter beside her. "Come, Valer! Come and kneel down!" She wrung her hands and looked pleadingly at her husband.

Brother Iosif and I knelt down, too. Only Valer remained seated.

"Come, Valer!" Lavinia cried out passionately. "Please join us!"

Valer said slowly, "I am thinking, Lavinia. I do not want to go into something without weighing the cost completely. I see that this is serious."

My heart leaped for joy. Here was a man not easily swayed, yet the truth of the Gospel had definitely touched him. I prayed for his soul.

"Yes, Valer," Lavinia replied. "I am too hasty! But, oh! I want to repent! I do believe! Oh, brothers! Oh, men of God! Save us!"

"Lavinia," Brother Iosif said kindly. "We cannot save you. You must pray to God and confess your sins to Him. Only He can save you!"

"Yes," I encouraged her. "Open your heart and confess your sins to the Lord. Ask Him for forgiveness. Ask Jesus to come into your heart and cleanse you and make you a new person in Him."

Oh, how the seeking woman prayed! She poured out her heart to the Lord and confessed her sins. Then, humbly and with tenderness, she begged Christ to come into her heart and make her His child. Lamaita, too, prayed, and I was deeply moved by this young girl's sincerity and understanding. I could tell that whatever she had read in that book had moved her deeply. Both of us men prayed for Lavinia and for Lamaita. Then there was silence.

Valer still had not said anything. During his wife's prayer, he had slipped to his knees and joined our little circle. But he had offered no prayer of his own.

In that quiet time, we all waited. Finally, Lavinia could stand the silence no longer. "Valer, what are you doing?" she whispered lovingly to him.

"I—I am thinking," he replied.

"Valer, you need to pray," Lavinia urged him.

"If you want to pray, talk to God like you talk to us," I encouraged him. "God is more interested in hearing our heart than the words we say."

"Dear God," Valer began. Then his voice faltered. "I—I don't know how," he said looking at us. "I have never prayed in my life."

Again I encouraged him. "Valer, God is in this room. Even though you can't see Him, you can talk to Him like you talk to your wife. He understands everything you mean to say."

Hesitantly at first, and then with more confidence, Valer prayed. He, too, asked God to forgive his sins by the blood of Jesus Christ. Then, quietly, he invited Jesus to be Lord of his life.

By that time Lavinia was weeping with joy. Her prayers mingled with her husband's. Lamaita, too, was praying. All of us joined together in prayer.

Even though the evening was rapidly fading away, we were in no rush to leave. In fact, as soon as we mentioned leaving, Lavinia jumped up.

"No, no! You must not leave yet. We will have tea and doughnuts before you go!" She hurried off into the kitchen.

In Romania it is very impolite to refuse to eat with friends. And this family had just become more than friends, they were now our brother and sisters in Christ. We gladly consented to stay.

Joy rang through their humble village home. Lavinia bubbled over in her newfound faith and, in his own quiet way, Valer's face reflected the deep inner experience he had just gone through. Lamaita no longer wore the troubled look I had noticed earlier. Now, a warm smile played around her lips and her eyes were at rest.

Sitting around the table, sipping our tea, we were truly in a heavenly place. We encouraged them to continually come to God in prayer, and assured them we would be praying for them. I also promised to get a Bible for them if I could. Once more, we invited them to come to church when possible. I knew it meant over an hour's travel each way, but I felt they needed the fellowship.

"Yes, yes! We will come!" Lavinia said impulsively, then checking herself, she looked at Valer. "If that is what you think we should do!"

Valer nodded his head immediately. "Yes, we will come to church as often as we can."

Somewhere, a clock chimed nine times. I looked at Brother Iosif and he nodded to me.

The banging at the front door startled us all. Three loud knocks came clearly through the entrance hall to where we were sitting.

For an instant, no one moved. We sat like a group of statues.

Then Lavinia spoke. "Valer! Go see who is at the door!"

Before Valer could leave the table, the door burst open. A large policeman entered, followed by another.

Lavinia jumped to her feet. "Officer *Varcaru*! What is the meaning of this?" she asked impetuously.

"I am the one to ask the questions," Officer Varcaru said loudly. Looking at Brother Iosif and me, he asked sternly, "Who are these people?"

"They are our friends. We invited them to our house!" I could hear the indignation in Lavinia's voice.

"What is going on in here?" With piercing eyes, the officer looked all around the room. "Why are you gathered together like this? Who gave you permission to have a meeting here?" Then he stared at me and asked, "Who are you?"

"I am Victor."

"You have no permission to have meetings in our village. Who is this man with you?"

"This is Iosif, my friend."

"You have violated the law. You came here as strangers and did not announce that you intended to hold a meeting in a private house. You are under arrest!"

"We are not having a special meeting!" Lavinia protested. "We invited them here! We are having tea together!"

"You, Valer! You come with these men to the police station!"

"I will come, too!" Lavinia burst out. She rose to follow us out.

"No!" Officer Varcaru roared.

"I want to go with my husband! I will come!"

Rising in indignation at having his authority challenged, Officer Varcaru lifted his beefy hand and slapped Lavinia on the face.

"Oh!" a startled cry burst from Lavinia. She lifted her hand to her stinging face.

Instantly, Valer was between his wife and the officer. He looked steadily at Officer Varcaru. For a moment, I thought Valer was going to strike the policeman, but suddenly I saw a calmness come over the recently-converted man.

"Lavinia, stay here." Then turning to the policeman, he said, "Leave the women alone. We will come with you to the police station."

"Yes," the officer sneered, "you will come." Rudely, he grabbed my arm with one hand. Seeing my briefcase, he grabbed it with his other hand. He propelled me down the hall and out the door. The other policeman followed with Iosif and Valer.

A black car was waiting by the gate. Unceremoniously, they shoved us into the back seat and drove the short distance to the police station.

A group of seven villagers were waiting for us there. Three women and four men were gathered around the conference table in the council room. We took the empty chairs at one end of the table, the policemen sitting on either side of us.

"Here are the witnesses who testify that you had an illegal meeting in our village," the officer announced. "They saw you together, and they came to report." Once again he asked me, "Why did you come to our village?"

"I came because I was invited. I am a pastor. If someone invites me to their home, I try to honor the invitation."

"You do not have permission to come into our village!" Officer

Varcaru screamed at me. "You must request permission from us before you come in here. Who do you think you are? You are a wolf coming in to steal our sheep. We have our own priest. We do not need you!"

Shifting his bulk in his chair, he addressed Valer seated in the chair beside him. "Valer, why did you invite these troublemakers here? You will suffer for this!" With a swipe of his huge hand, he slammed Valer's head against the tabletop.

Valer lifted his head and looked at his antagonist. "If I have to be killed because I invite people into my house, I guess you have to kill me."

"Shut up!" Varcaru screamed. He reached up and slapped Valer on the side of his face.

Opening my briefcase, he lifted out my Bible. Then he grabbed my songbook and shuffled through the pages. Glaring at me, he said, "You don't know that in this village we have people who see everything. If you think you can come here and cause trouble for us, you will be sorry you ever came." His voice rose in a cold fury. "You come into this village with your Book and try to take these sheep away from their true shepherd!"

I tried to duck, but I was too slow. His blow caught me on the side of my face. "I will make sure you never come back here again!" Another blow made my ear ring. "We will fine you and Valer so much that you will never let your shadow darken these streets!" Again he slapped me.

The villagers also began screaming. "You are too easy on him," they yelled at Varcaru. "Give him to us and we will use fence rails to beat him! Then he will never come back here again!"

I felt extremely vulnerable. Facing the enraged villagers and the policemen, I sensed that I was at their mercy. I could taste blood in my mouth from where a slap had cut the inside of my cheek against my teeth. My one eye felt strange and puffy.

Varcaru jerked me to my feet. He pushed me into the small room where Valer and Iosif had been taken. I hadn't even realized they were taken out.

"Come here!" Varcaru snarled at Iosif.

"God be with you!" I whispered to Iosif as he was taken back out to the others. Then the door was shut and Valer and I were by ourselves.

The shouting from the villagers and the resounding slaps carried clearly to us. We winced at every slap.

I looked at Valer. The side of his face was already showing the bruise marks of the policeman's hand. One of his eyes was starting to swell shut.

"Brother," I said softly to him. "I am sorry that right from the beginning you have to suffer. However, Jesus told us that all who will live Godly will suffer persecution. Do not despair."

Valer looked at me calmly. He did not say anything.

"Will you be faithful, brother?" I asked.

"I am not one to begin something and then back out of it when the going gets rough. When I told the Lord that I will serve Him, I meant it."

My heart leaped with joy! "Praise God, Valer! God will surely bless your steadfastness!"

It was midnight when we were finally pushed into the dark night. They had taken our names and addresses, and given us heavy fines and a final warning.

"We don't want to see another 'Christian' of your sort in this village! The treatment you got tonight is mild to what you will get if you ever come back again!" With an oath, Varcaru had told us to leave.

Brother Iosif and I turned toward the train station. Valer walked with us.

Scarcely had we left the police station when a woman slipped out of the shadows and joined us. It was Lavinia.

With a cry of alarm, she looked at Valer's bruised face. "Oh, Valer! They have hurt you!"

"Sh!" Valer quieted her. He took her arm, and we walked briskly on down the street.

At their gate, we bid them good-bye. "Thank you so much for coming!" Lavinia said with tears. "I am sorry you were treated this way in our village, but oh, we are so glad you came! For when you came, God came!"

We shook their hands, wished them God's blessings, and left.

Together, Brother Iosif and I rejoiced that three more souls were added to the kingdom. The beatings and persecution we had experienced were as nothing compared to the joy that welled up within us. During the long wait for the next train and all the way home, we praised God.

It was almost five o'clock by the time I reached our front door. Soon it would be time for me to leave for the factory where I worked. I had lost a night of sleep, but it had been worth it.

Scarcely had my shoes touched the stoop in front of our door when my wife, *Mihaela*, came bursting out. "Victor! We have been waiting for you all night! I have been so worried." She paused. "Why, Victor, you are smiling all over!"

I drew her inside and shut the door. "Don't turn on the light, let the children sleep. Come, dear, I have much to tell you. Three more souls are added to the kingdom of God!"

I did not tell her about the arrest until later. That was not the important news. The important news was that Valer, Lavinia and Lamaita had repented from their sins and turned their lives over to Jesus Christ.

When I returned to visit the new Christians two days later, I was welcomed with gladness. Together we committed ourselves into the care and protection of the Lord Jesus Christ. We spent time in reading the Bible and in fellowship. God truly kept His hand over us. I don't know if the neighbors found out about my visit, but no one bothered us.

The following Thursday when we had our midweek meeting at our church, I saw the happy Lamaita, the radiant Lavinia, and the steadfast Valer sitting among the worshipers. I could tell that they drank in every word and eagerly followed along with the singing the best they could. After the service, my wife and I were able to visit with them before they left for their village.

So it was for the next two years, though not always without trouble or persecution. The villagers from Gircina did not let up on their hostilities. At times the little family was refused admittance on the bus when they wanted to come to church. Bad words were showered on their defenseless heads when they were caught on the street. They were mocked, scorned and threatened.

None of these things moved them. Lavinia especially had a great yearning to know more about the Christian walk of life. More than once she made the lengthy journey to our house, where she would ask questions, probe into the meaning of the Scriptures, and fill her hungry soul with our fellowship.

"Unless a seed falls into the ground, and dies, it cannot grow. We all know this from our experiences with our gardens. Every little seed planted into our Romanian soil has to die first. But from that death comes life!

"When we die to self and let the Lord Jesus Christ make us a new person, spiritual life begins! We die to self, and live unto Jesus!

"Sister Lavinia understood this. She willingly gave up her old self, died to the old Lavinia, and God gave her the new birth. Many of you knew her. Many of you saw what happened to her life. You saw the change that came to her home. You saw what happened to Brother Valer and to Sister Lamaita. Christ came into their home!

"Now our sister has departed from this life. Her body has died, but her soul is free! Free to go home to our Lord and Savior, Jesus Christ! Free from her cancer-ridden body, free from the terrible pain she endured, free from all sin!"

I paused and looked over the audience. More than 200 people were crowded into the courtyard of Valer's house. Lavinia's body, clothed in white, lay in front of me. Valer and Lamaita were in the front row. Behind them, Christians who had come from all around the area stood listening intently. At the edge of our group, curious villagers listened apprehensively, moving about nervously.

"Sister Lavinia was ready to go," I continued. "Yes, in her final days, her pain became more intense, her body more restless. But in her spirit, she had peace. Her faith was in the Lord Jesus Christ and in what He has done for her and her family.

"When she asked us to conduct her funeral, she requested that we do not mourn like those who have no hope. Yes, we do grieve that she has left us here, for we will miss her, but our joy is far greater in knowing that she has gone to her eternal home. And someday, all of us who have our sins washed away by the blood of the Lamb will join her there!"

Lamaita's eyes glistened with tears, but she was smiling. Oh, how she had learned to love her mother! The close ties between mother and daughter would surely bring pain from the separation. But I knew that this young girl had a deep inner strength that would carry her triumphantly on.

Valer, too, was deeply moved. I had learned to appreciate this dear brother very much. Though not quick to make decisions, once he was convinced that God wanted him to do something, he was as steadfast as a rock. For he was anchored to the Rock, Jesus Christ.

The Christians began to sing:

"How beautiful heaven must be!
   Sweet home of the happy and free!
Fair haven of rest for the weary,
   How beautiful heaven must be!"

Lavinia had requested songs for her funeral. For us Christians, this was one of the times we did not have to worry about trying to keep our service a secret. Hardly ever did authorities interrupt a funeral, no matter how openly we preached the Gospel.

On the way to the cemetery, we stopped and sang in front of the mayor's office. We continued singing as we followed the body out to the edge of the village. At the crossroads, we stopped and sang. More and more curious villagers, drawn by the singing, followed us.

The open grave was outside the cemetery fence. The officials in charge had not allowed Valer to bury his wife's body inside. Since she had become a "repentant," they said, her body must be buried on the outside along with those who had committed suicide.

Lavinia had known about this. She had told us, "I know they will not allow my body to be buried inside the cemetery fence. But I don't care! I will not be there, only my body!" She had turned to her daughter and to her husband. "Dear ones! I don't care where you bury my cancer-ridden body! Even if you have to place it on the roof! My soul will be at home with my Lord and Savior, Jesus Christ! Oh, I long to see Him! I am ready to fall at His feet and thank Him for all He is doing for me! I am ready to go home!"

For a while after the funeral, Lamaita lived with us. Lavinia had requested that, and Valer gladly gave his approval. They both knew that while Valer was at work, the young, fourteen-year-old girl was very vulnerable to danger. It was only later, after the Holy Spirit began moving among the villagers in Gircina, that she returned to live with her father.

Yes, God was not done with this village. Such a stirring testimony had this woman of God that a year after Lavinia's departure for heaven, a fledgling church was started in Gircina. Valer gladly opened his home for the villagers who came seeking the truth of the Gospel. Souls repented and turned to the Lord.

My wife and I feel greatly blessed to have been among Lavinia's friends. She has been an inspiration to so many. As we think back over her brief life as a Christian, we can truly say that Lavinia's influence will be felt among all of us for a long time.

15

Revival in the City

*Sometimes we wonder if the seemingly heartless officers in uniform
ever struggle with pity for the people who suffer for their faith.
But when God moves, things occur that are truly phenomenal!*

In the year 1988, the country of Ukraine was having a great
celebration. This was the thousandth anniversary of the intro-
duction of the Orthodox religion in the country.

The capital city *Kiev* was bustling with preparation to celebrate
the event. The city fathers were anticipating speeches, parades,
and a splendid display of marches from all the high church officials. Even though this was a communist nation, the leaders would
use this event to showcase to all the world their tolerance, even
support, of the state religion.

Winds of change were blowing over the Soviet Union. A great
tremor of unrest swelled within the hearts of the populace and
more and more voices raised to clamor for personal liberty. There
were even rising demands for independence. Independence from
Russia, the mighty northern neighbor that dominated every aspect
of political and even private lives! Truly, change was in the air!

Thus it was that *Yura Petrovich*, pastor of an evangelical church
in Kiev, made a bold decision. Since the entire city was preparing
for this great event, he would conduct a special service in his
church the very day of this celebration!

Verily, this was a bold and daring plan. Not only was their

church not recognized by the State, and therefore considered illegal, they would also run the risk of further incurring the wrath of the Director of Religious Affairs.

This evangelical church, near the outskirts of the city, had been a long-standing thorn in the flesh for the Religious Affairs Director. For Yura to plan such a public meeting, especially during the city's day-long celebration of the Orthodox church, could certainly be thought of as a deliberate act against authority.

Yet, Yura reasoned with himself, this was an unsurpassable opportunity. Multitudes of people would be in the streets, watching the parade and listening to the speeches. The KGB would have a challenge to monitor the movements and activities of thousands of people. Thus, those attending the special service in the evangelical church should be able to attend without being detected. Their movements would be hidden by the large crowd.

But even more, Yura felt the Spirit pressing him to do it. There was a great spiritual hunger among the citizens of Kiev as more and more seekers came to church on Sunday mornings. Truly, the fields were white for harvest. This was the time to launch his idea.

Yura shared his daring vision with the other ministers in the church, and they supported it whole-heartedly.

They made plans to hold two services simultaneously. One would be held at the meeting house on Pukhova Street The other service would be an open air meeting nearer to the center of the city.

A week before the scheduled event, the church leaders asked for assistance from the laity. Two thousand invitation cards had been printed, inviting the people of the city to come and hear the Gospel of the Lord Jesus Christ.

Eager hands reached for stacks of invitations. Yes! They would be happy to pass them out!

In spite of the city's preoccupation with the national celebration, the news of the planned meetings by the evangelicals reached the Director of Religious Affairs. Filled with wrath, he immediately sprang into action.

When Yura answered the urgently ringing telephone at his home, he at once recognized the voice of the Director of Religious Affairs. "These meetings you are planning will not be held!" the powerful man fumed. "I will not give permission for you to hold insurrectionist meetings during this national holiday! Or ever! If you do not obey this order and call off all gatherings, you will suffer the full consequences of the law!" The director slammed down the phone.

Yura shared this threat with the rest of the ministers. After prayer, they were filled with strength by the Holy Spirit as He showed them what to do. Thus a delegation of three ministers went to the office of Religious Affairs.

"Sir," they declared, "we will have the meetings. This is a holiday for the people, and we have the right to invite them to come and listen to the Gospel of Jesus Christ. We are not forcing anyone to come against their will. We are not breaking the law. We are not inciting unrest among the people against the government." Again, the Holy Spirit came upon them and filled them with power. They continued, "We must do what is right. We will obey our consciences and be true to our Lord."

Their boldness bewildered the director. Then he ordered them out of his office.

The day before the planned meeting, the director himself visited Yura. "Where are you having the meetings?" he demanded.

"Sir," Yura answered, "you have seen the invitation cards. You know where the meetings will be held."

"And where will you conduct the baptisms?"

Yes, the director was well acquainted with the practices of this evangelical group. Yura knew informers kept the director abreast of all the happenings. Years of experience had taught them that at these special events, many would come forward and join the group. After the meeting, those who repented would be baptized. Nothing enraged the officials more than the baptismal services the believers held.

"In the *Dnieper* River," Yura said plainly.

"Where in the Dnieper?"

"I can show you if you take me there," Yura replied.

There was something different about this encounter. It was clear that the director was as adamant as ever against them holding the meetings. He was not willing to allow any such gathering to take place yet, even with his great authority, he seemed powerless to stop it.

Yura did not ponder long over the unusual episode unfolding before him. The director arranged for a car to take them over the bridge to the planned baptismal site, and Yura willingly rode along.

Arriving at a large park, the driver stopped the car. Yura climbed out and walked to the broad, sandy beach in front of him. The wide waters of the Dnieper were calm in this backwater place, the current barely noticeable.

"Right here," he told the director. "We are planning to hold the baptisms here."

"No!" the man protested. "I will not give you permission for this! You will be prosecuted to the fullest extent of the laws of our country!" He strode furiously in front of Yura and glared into his eyes.

Then he turned and faced the river. He struggled for words. "This will be the last time you will use this spot. I will never give consent for you to use it again!"

Yura did not reply. Surely something beyond his understanding was happening! Why was the director so powerless? Why was he conceding that there would be a baptism here in this spot? Why had he said this would be the last time? By saying this, he was indicating there would indeed be a baptism here. Yura did not understand.

Yet, he kept silent. "Lord," he prayed, "I see Your mighty hand in this. Something is going on that I do not understand. I sense that You are in control of this entire situation. I give it all to You!"

The journey back across the river to Yura's apartment was silent. After he was dropped off, the car sped down the street.

In awe, Yura entered his doorway, eager to tell his wife of the strange happenings.

––––––––––––

The next morning, hundreds of people crowded the street in front of the church. Yura had decided to come an hour before the service. When he arrived, he was amazed at the crowds already there, quietly waiting for the service to begin.

"Tell the believers to wait outside," he instructed the ushers.

"Allow as much room inside for the visitors as you can."

The thirty-member choir was already in place, ready to begin the service. People began filling the pews until all the benches were filled. Still more people came. The balcony was filled to capacity and even the steps were filled with people.

More than 700 people finally found room inside. They stood along the outside walls. They sat on improvised benches made from structural lumber. Even the windowsills provided space for some of the youth to sit.

" 'For God so loved the world, that he gave his only begotten Son, that whosoever believeth in him should not perish, but have everlasting life!' " The speaker chose the beloved text from John 3 to open his message. For over an hour he spoke of man's sinfulness, of the love of God in sending His Son to earth, and of the saving grace that Jesus extends to all those who believe in His name.

In spite of the crowded conditions, the people paid rapt attention. Those standing outside the open windows strained to hear. The autumn sun shone warmly down on the crowd, and yet, hardly anyone left.

The very air was charged with vitality. As the story of Christ unfolded, everyone was caught up in the compelling drama. People began to weep as the speaker spoke of the agony Christ suffered in the garden. All during the saga of the crucifixion, hardly anyone stirred. They saw the barren hill and the three crosses, cringed at the pain of the nails, wept with the women and the disciples, and felt the horrible darkness that came over all the earth.

How the listeners strained to hear of the resurrection of Jesus. They thrilled to the story of Mary Magdalene finding Him outside the tomb! Excitement ran through the crowd as they heard of the disciples first seeing Him standing in the midst of them!

But the speaker did not stop there. He told the audience of the ascension of Christ, of the disciples' wait for the Holy Spirit, and then he told them of Pentecost.

"This is for you today! Today, you too can come to Christ and have His cleansing blood cover your sins! You can have the same thrill that the thousands experienced when the Holy Spirit came upon that crowd!

"Come to Jesus, and leave your sins behind! Repent, believe on Him, and you shall be saved!"

The choir, sensing the working of the Spirit, began to softly sing an invitational song.

"If you want to be delivered from your sins, if you want Jesus to cleanse you and set you free from your wicked life, come kneel here and cry out to God."

There was a ripple of movement in the crowd. Threading their way forward, people responded to the call of God.

It was an awesome moment. Tears streaming down their faces, men and women came forward, knelt on the floor and began praying for God's mercy on their souls. Young people, weeping for their sins, pushed their way to the front to join those already kneeling there.

The space between the front pew and the platform was filled with kneeling people. Yura and the other ministers moved among them, praying with the repentant souls. The choir ended their song and began to pray.

Voices ascended upward. The prayers of the sinners revealed their anguish. With streaming eyes, they cried out to the Savior. Still more people came forward.

Kneeling figures filled the aisles. There was no more room at the front. Still, people came forward.

Some people cried out to God from where they were sitting or standing. Outside, people were kneeling on the sidewalks, crying and praying. The Christian brethren moved among them, praying with them, encouraging them, and praising God.

No one would ever know how many people repented that day. Perhaps some responded out of emotion, or because they felt bewildered by what was happening. Some may not have really understood what was happening, and responded simply because others did.

But the Holy Spirit ministered to every sincere, seeking heart. Prayers of repentance began giving way to prayers of praise. Hands were lifted to heaven as burdened hearts were freed from sin. Now tears of joy streamed down beaming faces.

"My dear people," the speaker called out, his face wet with joyful tears. The crowd quieted down. "God has visited us!"

A chorus of praise rose from the saved.

"Tomorrow, we will meet at the *Druzhby* Park by the Dnieper. All of you who have truly repented and want to seal your conversion with baptism, come! If you are willing to say 'No!' to Satan and the world, and 'Yes!' to Jesus Christ, come! If you want to make a public declaration of your faith, come! We will want to meet with as many of you as we can and hear your testimony." He gazed at the crowd, meeting as many eyes as he could. He raised his arms in blessing. "Go in peace. May the grace of Jesus Christ our Lord be with you."

At the open air meeting close to the center of the city, the scene was the same. The same holy hush upon the audience, the same rapt attention to the wonderful story of Jesus, and the same outpouring of response from the crowd. The same Spirit was at work, and many repented of their sins and found salvation in Jesus!

At first it was with dismay that Yura saw the scores of KGB officers and police the next morning in Druzhby Park. He was keenly aware that what had happened the day before had not gone undetected. In fact, among the crowds of listeners, there had been plainclothes policemen keeping close watch over the entire proceedings. No, these things had not been done in secret. Yura knew that.

So, when he saw the military police, at first his heart sank. But soon, he and all the other ministers were thankful for their assistance. They needed it.

The huge park was filled with people. Thousands of them. Tens of thousands!

People were everywhere. The police cleared an area for the elders to gather with those desiring baptism. They roped off an area for the deacons to hang sheets for dressing rooms. And when the pastor addressed the crowd, the chief of police himself handed him a megaphone!

Raising his voice, the speaker again briefly told the story of salvation. He explained to the listeners that the men, women, and young people desiring baptism were making a public declaration of their faith in Jesus Christ.

As the group of applicants disappeared into the dressing rooms and emerged in white clothing, a hush spread over the vast multitude.

The ministers led the way to the bank of the Dnieper. More than a hundred new believers followed, dressed in white. The crowds of onlookers pressed closer.

Standing in waist-deep water, the ministers waited. The presbyter spoke to the applicants, entreating them to have all their sins confessed, their hearts clean before the Lord.

Then, at a signal, they moved into the water. Kneeling down beside the elders, they were asked to declare their faith.

Time and again, the testimonies of the saved carried clearly to the listening crowd on the banks.

"We baptize you in the name of the Father, of the Son, and of the Holy Ghost!" In groups of five, they were baptized. The elders assisted them to their feet and another group took their place.

Again and again, the words floated across the water to the listeners. "Upon the confession of your faith, we baptize you in the name of the Father, the Son, and of the Holy Ghost!"

Water streaming from their faces, hair and clothes, the newly-baptized rose from the water and joined their brothers and sisters on the shore.

Songs of praise and joy rose from the believers. This was a precious time, a holy time. Lives were being changed and public testimonies of a living salvation were being given.

All the time, the military police were conspicuously there. They, too, heard the testimonies of the new Christians. They, too, saw the baptisms. They, too, felt the awesomeness of the moment.

They caused no trouble. Absolutely none. Instead, they helped as much as they possibly could.

Everyone marveled at the complete order and calm over the huge crowd the entire time during the baptism. And afterward.

For when the baptism was over, the pastor again addressed the crowd with the help of the megaphone. He urged the people to turn from their evil ways and believe on the Lord Jesus Christ. He urged them to repent from their sins and be saved.

Again, the people listened. Many felt a longing, a deep desire to be free from their sinful lives and turn to Christ. Some began to weep. Again, many repented of their sins and cried out for salvation.

The work of the Spirit was not over that day. The elders of the church continued to minister to the repenting. Nor was it over in the following days and weeks.

The evangelical churches were filled with people every Sunday. People crowded into the churches. Among the three and a half million inhabitants of Kiev, hundreds repented of their sins and were baptized.

The Druzhby Park along the Dnieper became known as the place where baptisms were held. In fact, the Director of Religious Affairs, the very man who at one time had said, "This will be the last time a baptism is held here," declared instead that this place would be a place where all churches could legally conduct their baptisms!

And they did! Large groups, often more than a hundred, were baptized there. The strong arm of repression against the Christians relaxed, and the evangelical churches grew and multiplied.

Three years later, Ukraine declared itself an independent country. Now the people could enjoy complete freedom of religion and worship God as they wanted. A new era had dawned.

Yura marveled and praised God as he saw the great changes take place in his city. Truly, this was not the work of man, but of God. God had changed the hearts of those in authority and had given them compassion for the people. The power of the Holy Spirit was seen in Kiev, just as it was in the days of the apostles and the early church.

Christian Aid Ministries

Christian Aid Ministries (CAM) was founded in 1981 as a non-profit, tax-exempt, 501(c)(3) organization. Established to be a trustworthy and efficient channel, CAM enables the church to minister to physical and spiritual needs around the world.

Annually, CAM distributes approximately 15 million pounds of food, clothing, Bibles and Christian literature, medicines, seeds, and other aid in Romania, Moldova, Ukraine, Haiti, Nicaragua, Liberia, and other countries. CAM also responds to international emergencies such as famines, wars, and natural disasters in various countries. In the USA, CAM helps rebuild in areas devastated by floods, tornadoes, or hurricanes through its Disaster Response Services program.

CAM's ultimate goal is to glorify God and enlarge His kingdom. ". . . whatsoever ye do, do all to the glory of God." (I Corinthians 10:31)

CAM is controlled by a 12-member Board of Directors and operated by a 3-member Executive Committee. The organizational structure includes an Audit Review Committee, Executive Council, Ministerial Committee, several Support Committees, and department managers. CAM is supported entirely by contributions from concerned individuals and churches (largely Amish and conservative-Mennonite) throughout the USA, Canada, Mexico, and a number of other countries.

CAM's international headquarters are in Berlin, Ohio. CAM has a 55,000 sq. ft. distribution center in Ephrata, Pennsylvania, where food parcels are packed and other relief shipments are organized. Next to the distribution center is our meat canning facility. CAM also operates four clothing centers—located in Indiana, Iowa, Illinois, and Ontario, Canada—where clothing, footwear, comforters, and fabric is received, sorted, and prepared for shipment overseas.

Aside from management personnel and secretarial staff, most of the work at CAM's warehouses is done by volunteers. Each year, volunteers at our warehouses and on Disaster Response Services projects donate approximately 100,000 hours.

CAM issues an annual, audited financial statement to its entire mailing list (statements are also available upon request). Fund-raising and non-aid administrative expenses are kept as low as possible. Usually these expenses are about one percent of income which includes cash and donated items in kind.

For more information or to sign up for CAM's monthly newsletter, please write or call:

Christian Aid Ministries
PO Box 360, Berlin, OH 44610
Phone: 330-893-2428
Fax: 330-893-2305

About the Author

Harvey Yoder is also the author of:
God Knows My Size!
War in Kosovo
They Would Not Be Silent
Not in Despair (published by *Christian Light Publications*)

Harvey has been married for 28 years to Karen (Anderson). They have five children (two married, one living in Honduras, one living in Iowa, one at home). Harvey was a schoolteacher for over 20 years. He and Karen live in the mountains of North Carolina in a small community conducive to writing.

Glossary

Romanian and Russian spellings, pronunciations, and meanings in alphabetical order.

Alexei* *(Ah lyek SYAY)*
Anatoly* *(Ah nah TOH lee)*
Andrei* *(Ahn DRAY)* — *Andrew*
Antonina Fyodorovna* *(Ahn toh NEE nah FYOH dohr ohv nah)*
Anya* (AH nyah) — *Anna*
Beniamin Branza *(Ben yah MIN BRAH zuh)*
Biblia* (BEE blee yah) — *Bible*
borscht* (BORSHCH) — *a very common soup in Ukraine which includes carrots, beets, potatoes, beans, onions, garlic, and pork*
Bucureşti *(Boo koo RESHSHT)*
Casian Dorin *(Kah see AHN Doh REEN)*
Ceauşescu *(Chow SHESS koo)*
Claudia *(Clou OO dee ah)*
Dnieper* *(DNYE per)*
Druzhby* *(DROOZH bee)*
dyadya* *(DYAH dyah)* — *uncle*
Feraru Gheorghe *(Feh RAH roo GEH ahr geh)*
Florescu Lucian *(Floh RES koo Loo chee UHN)*
George Vins* *(Gee OHR gee VEENZ)*
Gherghina *(Gehr CHEE nuh)*
Igor* *(EE gor)*
Ioan *(EE won)*
Iosif *(YOH seef)*
Ivan Ivanovich Golovaschenko* *(Ee VAHN Ee VAHN oh veech Goh loh VAH shchyen koh)* — *John, son of John; Slavic peoples use patronymics, an ending (i.e. "oh-veech") added to their father's name, as their second name*
Ivan Nickolaevich* *(Ee VAHN Nee kho LAH yeh veech)* — *John, son of Nicholas*
kasha* *(KAH shah)* — *porridge*
Kalashnikov* *(Kah LAHSH nee kohv)* — *a Russian machine gun*
Kiev* *(KEE yehv)* — *the capital city of Ukraine*
kolhoz* *(kohl KHOHZ)* — *collective farm*
Komsomol** *(Kahm soh MOHL)* — *the Communist organization for youth*

* Russian names/words

** See more info at end of glossary

Lămâița *(Luh muh EET zuh)*

Lenucu *(Leh NOO koo)*

Lenuța *(Leh NOOTS ah)* — *derived from Elena*

Lilya* *(LEE lyah)*

Lubov Timofeyevna* (*Lyoo BOHV Tee moh FYAY yev nah* — *Charity, daughter of Timothy*

Macovei *(Mah koh VAY)*

Magda *(MOG dah)*

Mălin* *(MAH leen)* — *a medium-sized city in Ukraine approximately two hours' drive west of the capital, Kiev*

mămăligă *(mah mah LEE gah)* — *cooked cornmeal*

Marcel *(Mahr CHEHL)*

Margareta *(Mahr gah REHT ah)*

Marina *(Mah REE nah)*

Mikhail Kobetz* *(Mee khah EEL KOH byetz)* — *Michael*

Mihaela *(Mee high EH luh)*

Misha* *(MEE shah)*— *short form of Mikhail*

Nadia* *(NAH dyah)* — *short form of Nadyezhda, means hope*

Natasha* *(Nah TAH shah)*

Nelu *(NEH loo)*

Pavel *(PAH vehl)* — *Paul*

Petru *(Pet ROO)*

Petrenko* *(Pyeh TRYEN koh)*

Petrovich* *(Pyeh TROH veech)*

Piatra Neamț *(PEE aht rah NEE ahmtz)*

Pioter Vasilyevich Khometz* *(PYOH ter Vah SEE lyeh veech Khoh MYEHTZ)* — *Peter, son of Basil*

Ploiești *(Ploy ee ESHT)*

Prelepa* *(Pryeh LYEH pah)*

Pukhova* *(POO khoh vah)*

Sasha* *(SAH shah)* — *short form of Alexander*

Șerban *(Shcher BAHN)*

Simionescu *(See mee oh NEHS koo)*

Slavic* *(SLAH veek)*

Stanislav* *(Stah nee SLAHV)*

Stuchyov* *(Stoo CHYOV)*

Sveta* *(SVYEH tah)* — *short form of Svetlana*

Svetlana Alexandrovna* *(Svyeht LAH nah Ah lyehk SAHN drohv nah)*

Tamara* *(Tah MAH rah)*

Tata *(TAH tah)* - Daddy
Tima* *(TEE mah)*
Trofim Afanasyevich Kuzmenko* *(Troh FEEM Ah fah NAH syeh veech
  Kooz MYEN koh)*
Tovarăşul Popescu *(Toh VAH rah shul Poh PES koo)*
Valentin *(Vah lyen TEEN)*
Valer *(Vah LAIR)*
Vanya* *(VAH nyah)* — *short form of John (Ivan)*
Văcaru *(Vah CAH roo)*
Vasile *(Vah SEE lay)*
Vasily Prutin* *(Vah SEE lee PROO teen)*
Viorica *(VEE oh REE cah)*
Vitaly* *(Vee TAH lee)*
Volodya* *(Vah LOH dyah)* — *short form of Vladimir*
Yevgeny* *(Yev GEH nee)* - Eugene
Yura* *Yoo rah)*

** The Komsomol (likely acronym of "Communistic Soviet Youth") was an organization for youth under the direct leadership of the Communist Party. Children entered the Young Pioneers at about grade five, and the Komsomol at grade eight.

It was a means of propagating the youth, and uniting them under a banner. If you were not a Komsomol member, you could hardly receive higher education, and consequently, secure a good job.

Children at school were placed under immense pressure to join the Young Pioneers and then the Komsomol. It was a name they were proud of and strove to bring honor to.

Through it, as can be expected, the Party sometimes exploited the labor of the youth. For example, in 1961 the Komsomol youth were sent to Kazakhstan to plow the sod and build cities there. The work was tremendously difficult, and the conditions they lived in appalling. However, when the Party spoke, the Komsomol moved. They were taught they had to sacrifice for others.